C000220700

HYPERION

OR

THE HERMIT IN GREECE

Published by

MELROSE BOOKS

An Imprint of Melrose Press Limited
St Thomas Place, Ely
Cambridgeshire
CB7 4GG, UK
www.melrosebooks.co.uk

FIRST EDITION

Copyright © India Russell 2016

The Author asserts her moral right to
be identified as the author of this work

Cover designed by Melrose Books
German text ed. Friedrich Beissner, Stuttgart 1958

ISBN 978-1-911280-32-3

All rights reserved. No part of this publication may be reproduced, stored in a retrieval system, or transmitted, in any form or by any means electronic, mechanical, photocopying, recording or otherwise, without the prior permission of the publishers.

This book is sold subject to the condition that it shall not, by way of trade or otherwise, be lent, re-sold, hired out or otherwise circulated without the publisher's prior consent in any form of binding or cover other than that in which it is published and without a similar condition including this condition being imposed on the subsequent purchaser.

Printed and bound in Great Britain by:
CPI Group (UK) Ltd, Croydon, CR0 4YY

FSC
www.fsc.org
MIX
Paper from
responsible sources
FSC® C013604

To Michael

by the same author

poetry
The Kaleidoscope of Time
The Dance of Life
Pattern & The Golden Thread
The Lane to Paradise
The Theatre of Dreams

story
Rory in Dreamland

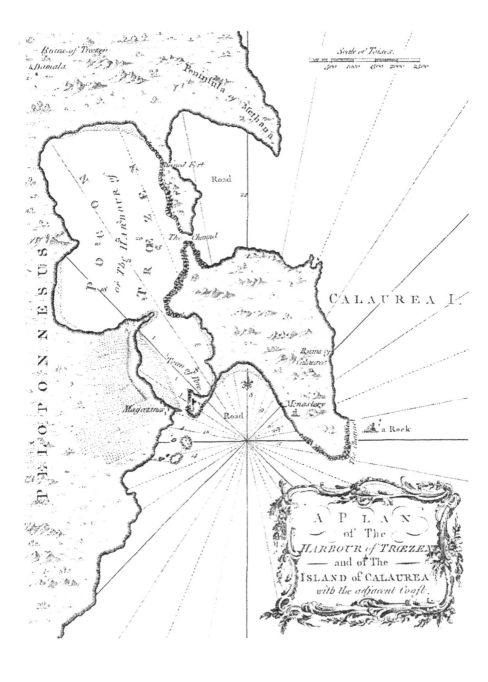

Ruins of Trœzen
Damala
Peninſula of Methana

Scale of Toises.
500 1000 1500 2000 2500

Ruined Fort
Road
The Chapel

PELOPONNESUS

PORT or THE HARBOUR of TRŒZEN

Town of Poro

Magazina

CALAUREA I.

Ruins of Calaurea

The Monastery

Road

a Rock

The Chapel

A PLAN
of The
HARBOUR of TRŒZEN
—— and of The ——
ISLAND of CALAUREA
with the adjacent coast.

HYPERION

OR

THE HERMIT IN GREECE

a translation of
HYPERION
ODER
DER EREMIT IN GRIECHENLAND
von
FRIEDRICH HÖLDERLIN

by
INDIA RUSSELL

CONTENTS

Illustration

Map of Calaurea, Greece   *Frontispiece*

Calaurea is Hölderlin's setting for the home of Hyperion's Diotima, from *Travels in Greece* 1776 by Richard Chandler which, together with *Travels in Asia Minor*, form much of the background to *Hyperion*.

HYPERION

OR

THE HERMIT IN GREECE

FIRST VOLUME

Non coerceri maximo, contineri minimo,
divinum est.

PREFACE

I would like to promise this book the Germans' affection. But I fear some will read it like a compendium and concern themselves too much with the *fabula docet*, whilst the others will take it too lightly, and neither will understand it.

He who merely sniffs at my plant, knows it not, and he who picks it, merely to learn from it, does not know it either.

The resolution of dissonances of a certain character is neither for mere reflection nor for vain pleasure.

The scene where the following took place is not new, and I confess, in this respect, I was once childish enough to try and change the book but I convinced myself that it was the only setting for Hyperion's elegiac character, and I was ashamed that the probable judgement of the public made me so excessively malleable.

I regret that critical examination of the plan is not possible for everyone at the moment. But the second volume shall follow as quickly as possible.

FIRST BOOK

HYPERION TO BELLARMIN

The dear native soil gives me once more sorrow and joy.
Every morning now I am on the heights of the Corinthian Isthmus and like the bee amongst flowers, my soul often flies to and fro between the seas which to the right and left cool the feet of my glowing mountains.

Particularly one of the two bays would have given me pleasure had I stood here a thousand years earlier.

Like a triumphant Demigod undulated the glittering bay, there between the glorious wilderness of Helicon and Parnassus, where the rosy dawn plays around a hundred snowy peaks, and the paradisian plains of Sicyon, in towards the City of Joy, youthful Corinth, and poured out the captured riches of all the zones before its belovèd.

But what is that to me? The cry of the jackal that sings its wild dirge amongst the stone heaps of antiquity startles me out of my dreams.

Happy the man whose heart is strengthened and delighted by a flourishing homeland. To me, it is as if I were being thrown into a morass, as though the coffin lid were closing over me, if someone reminds me of that which is mine, and if someone calls me a Greek, always it is as though he were throttling me with the collar of a dog.

And see, my Bellarmin! if occasionally such a sentiment escaped me, probably also in anger a tear came to my eye, then came the wise men who so gladly haunt you Germans, the wretches, for whom a suffering soul is just right for their maxims, then they enjoyed themselves and took it upon themselves to say to me: do not complain, act!

Oh, if only I had never acted! how much richer I would be in hope! —

Yes, just forget that there are people, suffering, assailed and thousandfold vexed heart! and return again from whence you came, to the arms of Nature, the changeless, still and beautiful.

HYPERION TO BELLARMIN

I have nothing of which I may say it is my own.

Distant and dead are my loved ones, and through no voice do I learn anything more of them.

My affairs on earth are finished. I went full of will to work, have bled for it and made the world not a penny richer.

Without renown and lonely, I turn back and wander through my native land which lies like a garden of the dead far around, and perhaps there awaits for me the knife of the hunter who keeps us Greeks, like the animals of the forest, for his sport.

But you still shine, Sun of Heaven! You still become green holy Earth! The Rivers still rush into the Sea, and shady trees rustle in the midday. The rapturous song of Spring sings my mortal thoughts to sleep. The fullness of the all-living world nourishes and satisfies with drunkenness my starving being.

Oh blessèd Nature! I know not what happens to me when I lift my eyes before your beauty, but all the delight of Heaven is in the tears that I shed before you, the lover before the belovèd.

My whole being becomes quiet and harkens, when the tender wave of the Air plays about my breast. Lost in the blue expanse, I often look upwards into the Aether and down into the holy Sea, and it is as though a kindred spirit opened its arms to me, as though the pain of loneliness dissolved into the life of the Divine.

To be one with all, that is the life of the Divine, that is the heaven of man.

To be one with all that lives, in blessèd self-forgetfulness to return to the All of Nature, that is the peak of thoughts and joy, that is the holy mountain top, the place of eternal rest, where the midday loses its oppressiveness and the Thunder his voice and the turbulent Sea resembles a billowing cornfield.

To be one with all that lives! With this utterance Virtue puts aside its wrathful armour, the spirit of man its sceptre, and all thoughts vanish before the eternally-one world, like the rules of the struggling artist before his Urania, and brazen Fate renounces dominion, and from the covenant of beings death vanishes, and inseparableness and eternal youth beautifies and fills the world with bliss.

On these heights I often stand, my Bellarmin! But a moment's reflection casts me down. I consider and find myself as before, alone with all the pains of mortality and my heart's sanctuary, the eternally-one world, is gone; Nature closes her arms and I stand like a stranger before her, and understand her not.

Ah! had I never gone into your schools! Knowledge, which I pursued down into the depths, from which, youthfully foolish, I expected confirmation of my pure joy, that has destroyed everything for me.

I have become through you so absolutely reasonable, have thoroughly learnt to distinguish myself from that which surrounds me, am now solitary in the beautiful world, am so rejected from the garden of Nature where I grew and blossomed, and wither in the midday Sun.

Oh, a god is man when he dreams, a beggar when he reflects, and when enthusiasm has gone, he stands there like a wayward son, who has been thrown out of the house by his father, looking at the miserable pennies that compassion has given him for the way.

HYPERION TO BELLARMIN

I thank you for asking me to tell you about myself, that you bring former times into my memory.

That also drove me back to Greece, that I wanted to be closer to the play of my youth.

Like the worker into refreshing sleep, my assaulted being often sinks into the arms of the innocent past.

Peace of childhood! heavenly peace! How often I stand quietly before you in loving contemplation and like to think of you! But it is true, we only have concepts of that which once has been bad and made good again; of childhood, innocence, we have no conception. When I was still a quiet child and knew nothing of all that which surrounds us, was I not more than now, after all the troubles of the heart and all the thinking and struggling?

Yes! a divine being is the child as long as it is not dipped into the chameleon colours of men.

It is completely what it is, and therefore it is so beautiful.

The constraint of law and Fate does not touch it; in the child is freedom only.

In it is peace; it has still not fallen out with itself. Wealth is in it; it knows its heart, not the insufficiency of life. It is immortal for it knows nothing of death.

But men cannot tolerate that. The Divine must become like one of them, must learn that they are also there, and before Nature drives it out of its Paradise, men flatter and drag it out onto the cursèd field so that, like them, it may labour in the sweat of its face.

But it is also beautiful, the time of awakening, if only one does not awake us at the wrong time.

Oh they are holy days when our heart for the first time tries out its wings, when we, full of quick fiery growth, stand there in the glorious world, like the young plant when it opens itself to the morning sun and stretches its little arms towards the unending sky.

How it urged me about to the mountains and the seashore! ah how often I sat there with beating heart on the heights of Tenos, and followed with my eyes the falcons and cranes and the bold, joyful ships as they disappeared below the horizon! Down there! I thought, down there one day you also will wander, and I was like one who, languishing, throws himself into a cooling bath and pours the foaming water over his brow.

Sighing, I then turned again towards my house. If only the school years were over, I often thought.

Good youth! they will not be over for a long time.

That man in his youth believes the goal to be so near! It is the most beautiful of all deceptions with which Nature aids the weakness of our being.

And when often I lay there amongst the flowers and sunned myself in the tender Spring light and looked upwards into the clear blue that embraced the warm Earth, when under elms and willows in the lap of the mountain, I sat after a refreshing fall of rain, when the branches still trembled from the caresses of the Sky and above the dripping woods golden clouds moved, or when the evening star, full of peaceful spirit, rose with the ancient youths, the other Heroes of Heaven, and I thus saw how life in them moves on through the Aether in eternal effortless order, and the Peace of the World surrounded and delighted me so that I became attentive and harkened without knowing what was happening to me — do you love me, good Father in Heaven! I then asked quietly, and felt his answer so sure and blessèd in my heart.

Oh you to whom I called as though you were beyond the stars, whom I called Creator of Heaven and Earth, friendly idol of my childhood, you will not be angry that I forgot you! — Why is the world not needy enough for us to seek One more as well ?*

Oh if she is a father's daughter, glorious Nature, is the daughter's heart not His heart? Her innermost being, is it not He? But do I have it then? do I know it then?

It is as though I saw, but then I am startled again, as though it were my own form that I have seen, it is as though I felt Him, the Spirit of the World, like a friend's warm hand, but I awake and believe I have held my own finger.

* It is probably not necessary to remember that such assertions, as mere phenomena of the human psyche, should by rights scandalize no one.

HYPERION TO BELLARMIN

Do you know how Plato and his Stella loved each other?

Thus I loved, thus was I loved. O I was a happy youth!

It is gladdening when like associates with like, but it is divine when a great person draws the lesser up to him.

A friendly word from a brave man's heart, a smile wherein the consuming glory of the spirit is concealed is little and much, like a magic sign that conceals death and life in its simple syllable, is like a sacred water which springs from the depths of the mountain and imparts to us the secret power of the Earth in its crystal drops.

How I hate, in comparison, all the barbarians, who imagine they are wise because they have no more heart, all the rough monsters who thousandfold kill and destroy youthful beauty with their petty unreasonable discipline!

Good God! There the owl wants to drive the young eagles out of the nest, wants to show them the way to the Sun!

Forgive me, spirit of my Adamas! that I mention this before you. That is the gain that experience gives us, that we imagine nothing excellent without its mis-shapen opposite.

Oh if only you were eternally present to me, with all that is akin to you, lamenting Demigod of whom I think. He whom you surround with your peace and strength, conqueror and warrior, he whom you meet with your love and wisdom, let him flee or become as you. The ignoble and weak cannot exist in your presence.

How often you were close to me when you had long been away from me, transfigured me with your light and warmed me, so that my frozen heart moved again like the hardened source when the beam of Heaven touches it! To the stars I would have flown then with my blessedness, so that it would not become sullied by that which surrounded me.

I had grown up like a vine without a staff, and the wild tendrils spread themselves across the ground without direction. You know well how so much noble strength perishes here because it is not used. I drifted about like a will-o-the-wisp, grasped everything, was moved by everything, but only for the moment, and the helpless powers exhausted themselves in vain. I felt that everywhere I was missing something and yet still could not find my goal. So he found me.

On his material, the so-called cultivated world, he had expended patience and skill for long enough, but his material was and had remained stone and wood, probably assumed of necessity the outward noble form of man, but there was nothing my Adamas could do with it; he wanted men, and to create these he had found his art too poor. They had been there once, those he sought whom his art was too poor to create, that he clearly recognised. Where they had been, he also knew. There he wanted to go and beneath the ruins enquire after their Genius, to shorten for himself the lonely days. He came to Greece. Thus I found him.

I can still see him walking towards me in smiling contemplation, I can still hear his greeting and his questions.

Like a plant when its peace soothes the striving spirit, and simple sufficiency returns to the soul — so he stood before me.

And I, was I not the echo of his quiet enthusiasm? did not the melodies of his being sound again in me? What I saw I became, and it was divine what I saw.

How poor indeed is the most good-willed industry of man

against the omnipotence of undivided enthusiasm.

It does not stay on the surface, does not seize us here and there, needs no time and no medium; law and force and persuasion it does not need; on all sides and in all depths and heights it seizes us in the moment, and before we know it is there, before we ask what has happened to us, it transforms us through and through with its beauty, its blessedness.

Happy he who in this way meets a noble spirit in early youth!

O they are golden unforgettable days, full of the joys of love and sweet employment!

Sometimes my Adamas led me into the heroic world of Plutarch, sometimes into the magic land of the Greek Gods, sometimes he ordered and calmed my youthful striving with number and measure, sometimes he climbed the mountains with me; in the daytime to see the flowers of the heath and woods and the wild mosses of the cliffs, at night to see above us the divine stars, and to understand them in our human fashion.

It is a precious feeling of well-being within us when thus the inner self is strengthened, differs from and establishes a truer relationship with its subject, and our spirit gradually becomes capable of bearing arms.

But threefold I felt him and myself when we, like shades of a former age, with pride and joy, with anger and lament, ascended Mount Athos and from there took a boat across to the Hellespont and then down through all the quiet islands, to the shores of Rhodes and the abysses of Taenarum; when there, yearning drove us in over the coasts into the dark heart of the old Peloponnese, to the lonely banks of the Eurotas, ah! the extinct valleys of Elis and Nemea and

Olympia; when we there, leaning against a temple pillar of forgotten Jupiter, surrounded by oleander and evergreen, looked into the wild river bed and the life of Spring, and the eternally youthful Sun exhorted us to remember that man had also been there once and now was gone, that the people's glorious nature was hardly still there now, like the fragment of a temple or a picture of the dead in the memory — there I sat, sadly playing beside him and plucked the moss from a Demigod's pedestal, dug out a marble shoulder of a hero from the ruins, and cut the thorn bush and the heather from the half-buried architraves whilst my Adamas sketched the landscape, how, with comforting friendliness it surrounded the ruins, the hills of wheat, the olives, the herd of goats that hung on the mountain steeps, the elm forest which cast itself from the peaks into the valley; and the lizard played at our feet, and the flies buzzed around us in the stillness of the noon — dear Bellarmin! I wish I could tell you as nicely as Nestor; I traverse the past like a gleaner through the stubble fields when the lord of the land has reaped; then one picks up every straw. And as I stood beside him on the heights of Delos, what a day that was that dawned for me, when I climbed with him up the ancient marble steps in the granite wall of Mount Cynthus. Here lived the Sun God once, amid the glorious festivals where, like a golden cloud, assembled Greece glowingly surrounded him. In floods of joy and enthusiasm the Greek youths threw themselves, here, like Achilles, into the Styx, and like the Demigod, arose unvanquishable. In the groves, in the temples, their souls awoke and resounded in one another, and each faithfully preserved the enchanting chords.

But of what do I speak? As though we still had an intimation of those days! Ah! not even a beautiful dream can flourish beneath the curse that lowers over us. Like a howling North wind, the present travels over the blossoms of our spirit and parches them at source. And yet it was a golden day that surrounded me on Mount Cynthus! It was still dawning when we arrived up there. Now he arose in his eternal youth, the ancient Sun God, contented and effortless as always, the immortal Titan flew up with his thousand particular joys and smiled down on his desolate country, on his temples, his columns, which Fate had cast down before him, like the dry rose leaves which a child in passing thoughtlessly tore from a bush and strewed upon the earth.

Be like this! cried Adamas to me, grasped me by the hand and held it towards the God, and it was to me as though the morning wind carried us forth with it and brought us into the company of the holy Being who now climbed up to the zenith of the Heavens, friendly and great, and with his strength and his spirit wonderfully filled the world and us.

Still mourns and rejoices my inner being at each word that my Adamas said to me then, and I cannot understand my destitution, when often it is to me as it must have been then to him. What is loss, when man finds himself thus in his own world? In us is everything. What does it trouble a man then if a hair fall from his head? Why does he strive so for slavery when he could be a God! You will be lonely, dear one! Adamas also said to me then, you will be like the crane, whom his brothers leave behind in the raw season whilst they seek the Spring in distant lands.

And that is it, dear one! That makes us poor amidst all wealth, that we are unable to be alone, so that the love in us, for as long as we live, shall not die away. Give me my Adamas again and come with all who belong to me so that the ancient beautiful world will be renewed amongst us, so that we may assemble and unite in the arms of our divinity, Nature, and see! then I will know nothing of need!

But let no one say that Fate parts us! We it is, we! we have our pleasure in casting ourselves into the night of the unknown, into the cold strangeness of some other world, and were it possible, we would leave the Sun's sphere and rush out beyond the limits of the wandering star. Alas! for the wild breast of man no home is possible; and as the beam of the Sun again parches the plants of the Earth which he unfolds, so man kills the sweet flowers that flourished in his breast, the joys of relationship and love.

It is as though I scolded my Adamas that he left me, but I do not scold him. O indeed, he wanted to return!

In the depths of Asia there was said to be hidden a people of rare excellence; thither his hopes drove him further.

As far as Ios I accompanied him. They were bitter days. I have learnt to bear pain, but for such a parting I have no strength in me.

With every moment that brought the last hours nearer to us, it became clearer how interwoven this person was with my being. Like a dying man his fleeting breath, my soul held him.

At the grave of Homer we spent a few days, and Ios became for me the holiest of islands.

Finally we tore ourselves away. My heart had fought itself into tiredness. I was calmer at the last moment. I knelt before him, embraced him for the last time with these arms; give me a blessing, my Father! I cried softly up to him, and he smiled greatly, and his brow spread before the morning stars and his eye pierced the spaces of the Heavens — Keep him for me, he cried, you spirits of a better time! and raise him up to your immortality, and all you friendly powers of Heaven and Earth, be with him!

There is a God in us, he added more calmly, who, like streams, guides Fate, and all things are His element. Let Him be above all, with you!

Thus we parted. Fare well, my Bellarmin.

HYPERION TO BELLARMIN

Whither could I flee from myself, had I not the dear days of my youth?

Like a spirit which finds no rest in Acheron, I turn back to the forsaken places of my life. Everything ages and grows young again. Why are we excluded from the beautiful course of Nature? Or does it also hold true for us?

I would like to believe it if there were not One thing in us, that terrific striving to be All, that like the Titan of Aetna stormily erupts from the depths of our being.

And yet, who would not prefer to feel it in himself, like a seething oil, than admit to himself that he is born for the whip and for the yoke? A raging charger or a crestfallen jade, which is nobler?

Dear one! there was a time when also my breast sunned itself in great hopes, when also in me the joy of immortality beat in every pulse, when I wandered amongst glorious plans, as in a vast forest night, when, happy like the fishes of the ocean, I penetrated further, ever further into my shoreless future.

How courageously, blessèd Nature! the youth arose from your

cradle! how he delighted in his untried armour! His bow was strung and his arrows rustled in the quiver, and the Immortals, the great spirits of antiquity, led him and his Adamas was in the midst of them.

Where I went and stood, the glorious figures accompanied me; like flames, the deeds of all times merged in my senses, and as in one exultant storm, the colossal forms, the Clouds of Heaven, unite, so in me the hundredfold victories of the Olympiads were united, became one unending victory.

Who can bear it, who is not pulled down by the terrifying glory of the ancients, as a hurricane pulls down the young forests, when it seizes him as it did me and when, as I, he lacks the element within which he could gain a strengthening self-confidence.

O me, me like a storm, the greatness of the ancients bowed my head, tore away the bloom from my face, and often I lay there where no one saw me, in a thousand tears, like a felled pine which lies by the stream and hides its dying crown in the flood. How gladly I would have bought one moment of a great man's life with blood!

But how would that help me? Indeed, no one wanted me.

O it is wretched to see oneself so annihilated; and he to whom this is incomprehensible, let him not inquire thereafter, and let him thank Nature that she created him for pleasure like the butterflies, and go, and in his life nevermore speak of pain and misery.

I loved my heroes, like a fly the light; I sought their dangerous proximity and fled and sought it again.

Like a bleeding stag into the stream, I often threw myself into the whirlpool of pleasure to cool my burning breast and to bathe away the raging glorious dreams of fame and greatness, but what did that help?

And when often at midnight my burning heart drove me down into the garden beneath the dewy trees, and the cradlesong of the Spring and the dear Air and the moonlight calmed my senses, and so free and peaceful above me, the silver Clouds moved, and from the distance there sounded the echoing voice of the Sea, with what friendliness then all the great phantoms of its love played with my heart!

Fare well, you heavenly ones! I often said in spirit, when above me the melody of the morning light began with gentle tones, you glorious dead fare well! I would like to follow you, would like to shake off what my century gave me and break out into the freer realm of shades!

But I languish in my chains, and seize with bitter joy the miserable cup, which is handed to me for my thirst.

HYPERION TO BELLARMIN

My island had become too narrow for me since Adamas was gone. For years now I had been bored in Tenos, I wanted to go into the world.

Go first of all to Smyrna, said my father, learn there the arts of the sea and of war, learn the language of educated people and their conditions and opinions and morals and customs, test everything and choose the best! — Then by all means it can continue.

Learn also a little patience! added my mother, and I received this with thanks.

It is delightful to take the first step out of the bounds of youth, it is as though I thought of the day of my birth when I think of my departure from Tenos. There was a new Sun above me, and land and Sea and Air I enjoyed as for the first time.

The vital activity with which I now pursued my education in Smyrna, and the speedy progress calmed my heart not a little. Also many a blessèd evening I recall from this time. How often I walked under the ever green trees on the banks of the Meles to the birthplace of my Homer, and gathered votive flowers and threw them into the holy River! To the nearby grotto I went then in my peaceful dreams; there, they say, the ancient one had sung his *Iliad*. I found him. Every tone in me became silent in his presence. I opened his divine poem and it was as though I had never known it, so completely differently it lived in me.

I like also to think of my wanderings through the regions of Smyrna. It is a glorious land, and a thousand times I have wished myself wings to fly once in the year to Asia Minor.

Out of the plain of Sardes, I ascended the cliff walls of Mount Tmolus.

I had stayed overnight at the foot of the mountain in a friendly hut amongst myrtles amid the scents of the labdanum bushes where in the golden waters of the Pactolus, the swans played at my side, where an ancient temple of Cybele looked out of the elms like a shy spirit, into the bright moonlight. Five dear columns mourned over the ruins, and a royal portal lay tumbled down at their feet.

Through a thousand blossoming bushes my path led now upwards. From a steep slope whispering trees bowed and showered my head with their delicate flakes. I had gone out in the morning.

At midday I was on the heights of the mountain. I stood, looked joyfully out before me, enjoyed the purer airs of the Sky. They were blessèd hours.

Like a sea lay the land from which I had come, there before me, youthful, full of living joy; it was a heavenly unending play of light with which the Spring greeted my heart, and as the Sun of Heaven discovered itself again in the thousandfold changes of light which the Earth returned to her, so my spirit recognised itself in the fullness of life which surrounded it, from all sides surprised it.

To the left, from the marble cliff that hung above me where the eagle played with his young, where the snow peaks shone up into the blue Aether, the river plunged and exulted like a giant, into the woods below; to the right, thunderclouds rolled towards me across the woods of Sipylus; I did not feel the storm they carried, only a little breeze in my locks, but their thunder I heard as one hears the voice of the future, and their flames I saw, like the distant light of the divined deity. I turned southwards and went on. There it lay open before me, the whole paradisian land through which the Cayster flowed through so many charming detours as though it could not linger long enough amongst all that richness and loveliness which surrounded it. Like the Zephyrs, my spirit wandered happily about from beauty to beauty, from the strange peaceful little village which lay deep under the mountain, as far as where the mountain chain of the Messogis dawned.

I returned to Smyrna like a drunkard from the feast. My heart was too full of goodwill, not to lend mortality of its excess. I had too happily captured within me the beauty of Nature not to fill the deficiencies of human life with it. My poor Smyrna clad itself in the colours of my enthusiasm, and stood there like a bride. The sociable towns attracted me. The absurdity of their customs amused me like a child's foolishness, and because by nature I was above all these introduced forms and customs, I toyed with them all, and put them on and took them off like carnival costumes.

But what really spiced the poor fare of the common round were the good faces and figures that here and there compassionate Nature still sends into our darkness like stars.

What heartfelt joy I had in them! with what belief I interpreted these friendly hieroglyphs! But it was almost with me as formerly with the birches in the Spring. I had heard of the sap of these trees and thought how wonderful, what a precious beverage the dear trunks must give. But there was not enough strength and spirit therein.

Ah! and how wretched was everything else that I heard and saw.

It was really to me, here and there, as though human nature had merged into the multiplicity of the animal kingdom when I went around amongst these educated ones. As everywhere, so also here the men were particularly demoralized and rotten.

Certain animals howl when they hear music. My better brought up people, on the contrary, laughed when there was talk of beauty of the spirit and youth of the heart. Wolves go away when a fire flames up. If those people saw a spark of reason then they turned their backs like thieves.

If I once spoke a warm word about ancient Greece, then they yawned and were of the opinion that one also had to live in the present time; and good taste had still not been completely lost, added another importantly.

This was then also demonstrated. The one affected wit like a deck-hand, the other puffed out his cheeks and preached maxims.

One, indeed, behaved as an enlightened one, snapped his fingers at the heavens, and cried that he had never cared for the bird in the bush, the bird in the hand, that was his preference! But when one spoke to him of death then immediately he put his hands together, and gradually turned the conversation to how dangerous it was that our priests no longer stood for anything.

The only ones of whom I could occasionally make use were the story-tellers, the living registers of foreign towns and lands, the talking peep-shows, where one can see mounted potentates and church towers and markets.

Finally I was tired of throwing myself away to seek grapes in the desert and flowers in the ice field.

I lived now more resolutely alone, and the gentle spirit of my youth was almost completely lost from my soul. The incurableness of the century had become so clear to me from so much that I relate and do not relate, and the beautiful consolation of finding my world in One soul, of embracing in a friendly form my kind, that also I lacked.

Dear one! what would life be without hope? A spark which leaps from the coal and is extinguished, and just as one hears at a gloomy time of year a gust of wind which howls for a moment and then dies away, would it be so with us?

Also the swallow seeks a friendlier land in Winter, the deer runs about in the heat of the day and his eyes seek the Spring. Who says to the child that the mother shall not refuse it her breast? And see! yet it seeks it.

Nothing would live if it did not hope. My heart now locked up its treasures, but only to save them for a better time, for the

Only One, Holy, True, that certainly, in some period of existence, should meet my thirsting soul.

How happily I often clung to it when, in the hours of presentiment, softly like the moonlight, it played about my calmed forehead. Even then I knew you, even then you looked at me from out of the clouds like a Genius, you who once in the peace of beauty rose for me out of the clouded wave of the world. Then it fought, then it burned nevermore, this heart.

As in silent air a lily gently moves, so my being moved in its element in the enchanting dreams of her.

HYPERION TO BELLARMIN

Smyrna was now spoilt for me. Really my heart had gradually become more tired. Occasionally, it is true, the wish could flare up in me to travel round the world or to enlist in the first war that came along, or to seek out my Adamas and burn out my ill humour in his fire, but with that it remained, and my meaningless fading life desired never to refresh itself.

The Summer was now soon at an end; I already felt in advance the melancholy rainy days and the whistling of the wind and the raging of the swollen streams, and Nature which like a bubbling spring, had risen in all plants and trees, already stood before my darkened senses, wasting and closed and introverted like myself.

Yet I wanted to take with me what I could of all the fleeing life, everything about me that I had grown fond of I wanted to save within me, for I well knew that the returning year would not find me again amongst these trees and mountains, and so I walked and rode now more than usual around the whole area.

But what particularly drove me out was the secret desire to see a person whom for some time I had encountered every day beneath the trees, by the gate where I passed.

Like a young Titan the glorious stranger strode thither amongst the race of dwarves, who with joyful shyness feasted on his beauty, scanned his height and his strength and, as on forbidden fruit, refreshed themselves with hidden glances at his glowing bronzed Roman head; and it was a glorious moment each time the eye of this person, for whose glance the free Aether seemed too confined, with pride put aside, sought and strove until it felt my eye and, blushing, we gazed after one another and passed on.

Once I had ridden deep into the woods of Mima and returned only in the late evening. I had dismounted and led my horse down a steep deserted path over tree roots and stones and as I thus wound through the bushes down into the hollow which now was revealed to me, a pair of Carabornian robbers suddenly fell upon me, and I had difficulty at first in holding off the two drawn sabres; but they were already tired from other work and so I managed. I calmly mounted my horse once more and rode down.

At the foot of the mountain in the midst of the woods and massy cliffs, there opened before me a small meadow. It became bright. The moon had just risen above the dark trees. A short way off I saw horses stretched out on the ground and men beside them in the grass.

Who are you? I cried.

That is Hyperion! cried a hero's voice, joyfully surprised. You know me, continued the voice; I meet you every day beneath the trees at the gate.

My horse flew like an arrow to him. The moonlight shone bright in his face. I knew him; I jumped down.

Good evening! cried the dear vigorous one, regarded me with a tender wild look and with his sinewy clenched hand pressed mine, so that my inner being felt the meaning of it.

O now was my meaningless life at an end!

Alabanda, so the stranger was called, now told me that he and his servants had been attacked by robbers, that the two whom I had come upon had been sent off by him, that he had lost the way out of the forest and therefore was compelled to remain where he was until I had come. I have lost a friend as well, he added and indicated his dead horse.

I gave mine to his servant and we continued on foot.

It served us right, I began, whilst we walked arm in arm together out of the forest; why then did we hesitate for so long and pass each other by until misfortune brought us together.

I must then say to you, however, replied Alabanda, that you are the more guilty, the colder one. I rode after you today.

Glorious one! I cried, just see! in love you shall never exceed me!

We became ever more intimate and joyful together.

Close to the town we came upon a well-built inn reposing amid plashing fountains and fruit trees and fragrant meadows.

We decided to stay the night there. We sat for a long time together at the open windows. Sublime spiritual peace surrounded us. Earth and Sea had become blissfully silent like the Stars that hung over us. A little breeze from the Sea, which flew into our room and played gently with our candle was scarcely there, nor the distant music from which the more powerful tones penetrated to us as the thundercloud rocked itself in the bed of the Aether and now and again sounded from afar through the stillness, like a sleeping giant when he breathes more deeply in his terrible dreams.

Our souls were bound to draw near the more strongly, because they had been closed against our will. We met each other like two streams which roll down from the mountains and cast off the burden of earth and stone and rotten wood and the whole inert chaos that had impeded them, to forge the way to one another and break through until where, seizing and seized with equal strength, united in one majestic River, they then begin the journey into the wide Sea.

He, by Fate and the barbarism of man, from his own home driven here and there amongst strangers, from early youth embittered and made wild and yet still with his innermost heart full of love, full of yearning to break out of the rough shell into a friendly element; I, already so profoundly cut off from everything, so with my whole soul foreign and lonely amongst people, so laughably accompanied by the clangour of the world in my heart's dearest melodies; I, the antipathy of all blind and lame and yet too blind and lame for myself, yet too deeply troublesome to myself in everything that was remotely connected with the sophists and the clever, the barbarians and the witty — and so full of hope, so full of the one expectation of a more beautiful life —

Were then the two youths not bound to embrace each other in joyful impetuous haste ?

O you, my friend and companion in arms, my Alabanda, where are you? I almost believe that you have gone over into the unknown land, to peace, have become once again as before when we were still children.

23

Occasionally, when a storm passes over me and distributes its divine powers amongst the woods and the crops, or when the waves of the Sea play amongst themselves, or a choir of eagles soars around the mountain peak where I walk, my heart can move as though my Alabanda were not far away; but more visibly, more real, more unmistakably he lives in me, exactly as he once stood there, a fiery, strict, terrible plaintiff as he named the sins of the century. How my spirit awoke then in its depths, how the thunderwords of inexorable justice rolled over my tongue! Like messengers of Nemesis our thoughts traversed the Earth and cleansed it, until not a trace of the curse was there.

Also the past we summoned before our tribunal, proud Rome did not frighten us with her glory, Athens did not bribe us with her youthful prime.

Like storms, when rejoicing, they rage unceasingly through woods and across mountains, so our souls penetrated forth in colossal plans; not as though, unmanly, we thought to create our world by a magic word and, childishly inexperienced, did not reckon with any opposition; Alabanda was too sensible and too brave for that. But often also effortless enthusiasm is warlike and wise.

One day is particularly present to me.

We had gone into the fields together, sat intimately encircled in the darkness of the evergreen laurel and looked into our Plato together, where so wonderfully nobly he speaks of ageing and rejuvenation, and rested now and then in the silent leafless landscape where the Sky, more beautifully than ever, played with the Clouds and sunshine around the autumnal sleeping trees.

We spoke thereupon much of present day Greece, both with

bleeding hearts, for the dishonoured ground was also Alabanda's homeland.

Alabanda was really unusually moved.

When I see a child, cried this person, and think how humiliating and demoralizing the yoke is that it will have to bear, and that it will be in want, like us, that it will seek people like us, that it will ask, like us, of Beauty and Truth, and that unproductively it will pine away like us, because it will be alone like us, that it — O just take your sons from the cradle and cast them into the flood to at least save them from your infamy!

Surely, Alabanda! I said, surely it will change.

By what means? he replied; the heroes have lost their fame, the wise their pupils. Great deeds if not perceived by a noble people, are nothing more than a powerful blow on a hollow forehead, and great words if they do not resound in great hearts, are like a dying leaf that rustles down into the mire. What do you want then?

I want, I said, to take a shovel and throw the mire into a pit. A people where spirit and greatness no longer produces spirit and greatness, has nothing more in common with others who are still people, has no more rights, and it is an empty farce, a superstition if one still wants to honour such will-less corpses, as though there were a Roman heart in them. Away with them! It must not be allowed to stand where it stands, the barren rotten tree, for it steals air and light from the young life which is ripening on towards a new world.

Alabanda flew to me, embraced me, and his kisses entered my soul. Companion-in-arms! he cried, dear companion-in-arms! O now I have a hundred arms!

That, at last, is for once my melody, he continued with a voice, that like a battle cry moved my heart, nothing more is needed! You have spoken glorious words, Hyperion! What? on the worm shall the God be dependent? The God In Us, for whom eternity opens a way, should stand and wait until the worm moves out of His way? No! no! One asks not whether you want! You have never wanted, you slaves and barbarians! One does not want to improve you either, for it is in vain! one will only take care that you get out of the way of mankind's career of victory. O! someone light me a torch that I may burn the weeds from the heath! prepare me a mine, someone, that I may blast the dull clods from the Earth!

Where possible one puts them gently to one side, I interrupted. Alabanda was silent for a while.

My joy is in the future, he finally began again and ardently grasped my two hands. God be thanked! I will come to no servile end. To be happy means to be sleepy in the mouth of the knave. To be happy! To me it is as though I had pap and tepid water in my mouth, when you speak to me of being happy. So foolish and so hopeless is all that for which you sacrifice your laurel wreaths, your immortality.

O holy Light that unrestingly active in his colossal realm moves there above us and also imparts his soul to me in the beams that I drink, your happiness be mine!

By their deeds the sons of the Sun are nourished; they live on victory; with their own spirit they incite themselves and their strength is their joy. —

The spirit of this person sometimes took hold of one, that one could have been ashamed, so feather-lightly one felt oneself carried away.

Oh, Heaven and Earth! I cried, this is joy! — These are other times, that is no tone from out of my childish century, that is not the ground where the heart of man pants beneath his driver's whip. — Yes! yes! With your glorious soul, man! You will rescue our country with me.

That will I, he cried, or perish.

From this day on we became to each other ever more holy and dear. Deep, indescribable seriousness had come upon us. But we were only the more blissful together. Only in the eternal pure tones of his being did each live and, simply, we strode ahead from one great harmony to another. Full of glorious austerity and boldness was our life together.

How is it then have you become so wordless? Alabanda once asked me smilingly. In the torrid zones, I said, nearer the Sun, the birds also do not sing.

But everything in the world ascends and falls, and man, with all his giant strength, holds nothing fast. I saw a child reach out its hand once, to catch the moonlight; but the light went calmly on its way. Thus we stand, and strive, to halt inconstant Fate.

O, could one only as quietly and thoughtfully regard it like the movements of the Stars!

The happier you are, the less it takes to destroy you, and the blessèd days as Alabanda and I experienced them are like a precipitous crag where your travelling companion needs only to touch you to cast you over the jaggèd peaks, immeasurably down into the twilight depths.

We had made a glorious journey to Chios, had had a thousand delights in one another. Like little breezes over the surface of the

Sea, the friendly magic of Nature held us in its sway. With joyful wonder one regarded the other without saying a word, but the eyes said, thus I have never seen you! So glorified we were by the powers of the Earth and the Sky.

We had also then, with bright ardour, quarrelled over many a thing during the journey; I had, as usual, also again this time, my heartfelt pleasure in watching this spirit in his bold eccentric course, how he so irregularly with such uninhibited cheerfulness and yet mostly so surely pursued his path.

We hastened, when we had disembarked, to be alone.

You cannot convince anyone, I then said with heartfelt love, you persuade, you favourably prejudice people before you begin; one cannot doubt when you speak, and he who does not doubt cannot be convinced.

Proud flatterer, cried he to that, you lie! but it is right that you admonish me! only too often have you made me irrational! For all the world I do not want to free myself from you, but often then it worries me that you should be so indispensable to me, that I am so bounden to you; and see, he continued, as you have me so completely, you shall know everything of me as well! We had not thought until now, with all the magnificence and joy, of looking back into the past.

He now related his fate to me; and it was to me thereby as though I saw a young Hercules in combat with the Megæra.

Will you now excuse me, he concluded the tale of his privations, will you now be calmer when often I am rough and offensive and unsociable?

Oh quiet, quiet! I cried, deeply moved; but that you are still here, that you kept yourself for me!

Yes indeed! for you! he cried, and it pleases me greatly that I am still then palatable fare for you. And if also I sometimes taste like a crab apple to you, then tread me until I am drinkable.

Forbear! forbear! I cried; I struggled in vain. The man turned me into a child; nor did I conceal it from him; he saw my tears and woe to him if he were not allowed see them!

We are indulging, began Alabanda again, we are killing time with intoxication.

These are our betrothal days together, I cried exhilarated, thus it may well still sound as though one were in Arcadia. – But to return to our previous conversation!

You then, however, cede to the state too much power. It should not demand what it cannot enforce. But what love gives and the spirit, that does not allow itself to be enforced. That let it leave untouched, or let him take his law and clamp it in the pillory! By Heaven! he who wants to make the state into a school of morals knows not what wrong he does. That man wanted to make it into a heaven has always made the state into a hell.

The rough shell around the seed of life, and nothing more, is the state. It is the wall around the garden of human fruits and flowers.

But what does the wall around the garden help, where the ground lies barren? There only the rain of Heaven can help.

Oh, rain of Heaven! O Enthusiasm! You will bring us back the Spring of Mankind. You the state cannot order hither. But let it not disturb you, then you will come, come you will with your all-powerful bliss, in golden Clouds will you veil us and carry us up beyond mortality, and we will wonder and ask if we are still those, we, the poor, who asked the Stars if a Spring blossomed there for us — would you ask me when this will be? Then, when the Belovèd of Time, the youngest most beautiful Daughter of Time, the New Church, comes forth out of these stained outmoded forms, when the awakened feeling for the Divine brings back to man his divinity, and to his breast beautiful youth, when — I cannot prophesy it, for I scarcely can divine it, but it will come surely, surely. Death is a messenger of Life, and that now our sick souls are sleeping in our bodies, this bears witness to an imminent, healthy awakening. Then, only then do we exist, then is the Element of Spirits found!

Alabanda was silent, and regarded me for a while amazed. I was transported by infinite hopes; divine powers carried me away like a little cloud —

Come! I cried, and grasped Alabanda by his garments, come, who can bear it any longer in the prison which benights us?

Whither, my enthusiast, replied Alabanda drily, and a shadow of scorn seemed to pass over his face.

It was as though I had fallen from the clouds. Go! said I, you are a petty person!

At the same moment several strangers entered the room, striking figures, mostly lean and pale, as far as I could see in the moonlight, calm, but in their mien was something that went through the soul like a sword, and it was as though one stood before the All-knowing; one could have doubted if this were the exterior of poor natures if here and there slain emotions had not left their traces.

Particularly one struck me. The stillness of his features was the stillness of a battlefield. Fury and love had raged in this person, and intellect shone above the ruins of his mind like the eye of the hawk that sits on shattered palaces. Deep contempt was on his lips. One sensed, that this person concerned himself with no meaningless purpose.

Another may have owed his peace more to a natural hardness of heart. One found in him hardly any traces of violence perpetrated by self-discipline or Fate.

A third may have wrung his coldness from life more with the power of conviction, and was probably still in conflict with himself, for there was a mysterious contradiction in his being, and it seemed to me as though he had to guard himself. He spoke the least.

Alabanda sprang up like taut steel at their entrance.

We sought you, cried one of them.

You would find me, said he laughing, were I to hide myself in the middle of the Earth. They are my friends, he added, turning to me.

They seemed to scrutinize me quite closely.

He is also one of those who would like to have things better in the world, cried Alabanda after a while, and pointed to me.

You are serious? one of the three asked me.

It is no joke to better the world, I said.

You have said much in a word! cried yet another of them. You are our man! another.

You think likewise? I asked.

Ask what we do! was the answer.

And if I asked?

Then we would say to you that we are here to cleanse the earth, that we pick out the stones from the field and shatter the hard clods with a mattock, and dig furrows with the plough, and grasp the weed by the root, cut it through at the root and together with the root pull it out so that it shall wither in the heat of the burning sun.

Not that we wish to harvest, joined in another; for us the reward would come too late; for us the harvest ripens no more.

We are in the evening of our days. We erred often, we hoped much and did little. We preferred to risk rather than reflect. We were keen to finish things and trusted in luck. We spoke much of joy and pain, and loved, hated, both. We played with Fate and it did the same with us. From beggar-state to crown it cast us up and down. It swung us as one swings a glowing censer, and we glowed until the coals became ashes. We have ceased to speak of luck and mishap. We have grown beyond the middle of life where it is green and warm. But that is not the worst that youth survives. From hot metal the cold sword is forged. Also it is said that on scorched, extinct volcanoes not a bad must grows.

We do not say that for our sake cried another then, somewhat more hastily, we say it for your sakes! We do not beg for the heart of man. For we do not need his heart, his will. For he is in no way against us, because everything is for us, and the fools and the clever and the simple and the wise and all vice and all virtues of coarseness and education are in our service without being hired, and blindly help towards our goal — we would only wish that someone could have the enjoyment of it, therefore we seek out the best from the thousand blind helpers, to make them into seeing helpers — but if no one wants to live where we built, it is not our fault or our loss. We did our part. If no one wants to gather where we ploughed, who blames us? Who curses the tree if its apple falls into the mire?

I have often said to myself, you are sacrificing to decay, and yet I completed my daily task.

These are deceivers! cried all the walls to my impressible senses. I was like one who, suffocating in smoke, breaks down the doors and windows to get out. I thirsted so for air and freedom.

They also soon saw how uneasy I was and broke off. Day was already dawning as I came out of the inn where we had been together. I felt the blowing morning air like balm on a burning wound.

I had already been too provoked by Alabanda's scorn, not to become completely doubtful of him because of his enigmatic companions.

He is bad, I cried, yes, he is bad. He feigns boundless trustworthiness and lives with such people — and hides it from you.

I felt like a bride, when she learns that her belovèd secretly lives with a low woman.

Oh, it was not the pain that one can cherish, that one takes to heart like a child, and sings to sleep with tones of the nightingale.

Like a furious snake, when it pitilessly winds upwards round the knees and loins and encircles all the limbs and then in the breast sinks its poisonous fangs and then in the neck, that was my pain, thus it clasped me in its terrible embrace. I summoned my highest heart to help, and fought for great thoughts in order to still remain calm, and indeed, after a few moments I succeeded, but now I was also strengthened to anger, now I also killed, like arson, every spark of love in me.

He must surely, I thought, they are certainly his people, he must be in league with them against you! What did he want from you anyway? What could he seek in you, the enthusiast? Oh, if only he had gone his way! But they have their peculiar pleasures in taking up with an opposite! to have such a foreign animal in their stable suits them quite well! —

And yet I had been so inexpressibly happy with him, had so often sunk in his embraces to awake from them with invincibility in my breast, had so often been strengthened and purified in his fire, like steel!

When I once on a clear midnight pointed out the Dioscuri to him, and Alabanda laid his hand on my heart and said: Those are only stars, Hyperion, only letters with which the names of the fraternal heroes are written in the Heavens; in us they are! living and true, with their courage and their divine love, and you, you are the son of the Gods, and share with your mortal Castor your immortality! —

When I roamed through the woods of Ida with him, and we came down into the valley to ask the silent grave mounds of their dead, and I said to Alabanda that amongst the grave mounds there was perhaps one that belonged to the spirit of Achilles and his belovèd, and Alabanda confided in me, how he was often a child and imagined to himself, that one day we would fall in *one* battle in a valley and rest together under *one* tree — who would have thought that then?

I reflected with all the strength of spirit that was left to me, I accused him, defended him and accused him again all the more bitterly; I struggled against my senses, wanted to cheer myself, and only became thereby full of gloom.

Oh, my eye had been wounded by so many a blow, had indeed hardly begun to heal, how could it now have more healthy glances?

Alabanda visited me the next day. My heart seethed as he entered, but I restrained myself, as much as his pride and his calm excited and inflamed me.

The air is glorious, he said finally, and the evening will be very beautiful, let us go together to the Acropolis!

I accepted. For a long time we spoke no word. What do you want? I finally asked.

You can ask that? replied the wild person with melancholy that pierced my soul. I was amazed, confused.

What am I to think of you? I finally began again.

That which I am! he replied calmly.

You need apology, I said in a changed voice and looked at him proudly, apologize! clear yourself!

That was too much for him.

How comes it then, he cried enraged, that this person should humble me as he pleases? — It is indeed true, I was let out of school too early, I had dragged all chains and severed all, only *one* was still lacking, there was only one still to be shattered, I had not yet been chastised by a capricious person — oh, complain! I have been silent too long!

Oh Alabanda! Alabanda! I cried.

Quiet, he retorted, and use not my name as a dagger against me!

And then also my ill humour broke loose completely. We did not rest until a return was almost impossible. We destroyed by force the garden of our love. We stood often and were silent, and would so gladly, with such thousand joys, have fallen on each other's neck, but unholy pride suffocated each tone of love which rose up from the heart.

Fare well! I cried finally and rushed away. Involuntarily I had to look round, involuntarily Alabanda had followed me.

Is it not true, Alabanda, I called to him, that is a strange beggar? his last penny he throws in the mire!

If that is so, then may he starve, cried he, and went.

I staggered on senselessly, stood then by the Sea and looked at the waves – ah! down there strove my heart, down there, and my arms flew towards the free flood; but soon there came upon me, as from Heaven, a more gentle spirit, and regulated my unruly suffering soul with its peaceful staff; I reflected more calmly on my fate, my belief in the world, my hopeless experiences; I considered people of manifold upbringings as I had experienced and known them from early youth, found everywhere dull or screaming discords, only in childlike simple limitation did I still find the pure melodies — it is better, I said to myself, to become a bee and build one's house in innocence, than to rule with the masters of the world, and, as with wolves, to howl with them, than to conquer peoples, and to stain one's hands with the impure material; I wanted to return to Tenos, to live amongst my gardens and fields.

You may smile! I was very serious. Does not the life of the world consist in the alternation of unfolding and closing away, in journeying from and returning to itself, why not also the heart of man?

Certainly the new teaching was hard for me, certainly I did not gladly depart from the proud errors of my youth — who also gladly tears out his wings? — but it had to be!

I carried it through. I was now really embarked. A fresh mountain wind carried me out of the harbour of Smyrna. With a wonderful peace, just like a child that knows nothing of the next moment,

I lay thus there in my ship, and regarded the trees and mosques of this town, my green ways along the shore, my footpath up to the Acropolis, I looked upon it and let it go, on and ever further on; but when I then came out onto the high Sea, and everything gradually sank down like a coffin into the grave, then all at once it was as though my heart had broken — O Heaven! I cried, and all life in me awoke and strove to hold the fleeting present, but it was gone, gone!

Like a mist lay the divine land before me where, like a deer on the open pasture, far and wide, I had roamed through the valleys and the heights, and brought the echo of my heart to the Springs and the Rivers, into the distance and the depths of the Earth.

In there, I had climbed the Tmolus in solitary innocence; down there where Ephesus once stood in its happy youth and Teos and Miletus, up there into holy mourning Troy, I had wandered with Alabanda, with Alabanda; and like a God, I had ruled over him, and like a child, tender and faithful, I had served him with joyful soul, with deep exultant delight in his being, always happy if I held his horse by the reins, or when beyond myself in glorious resolves, in daring thoughts, I met his soul in the fire of speech!

And now it was gone, now I was nothing more, was so wretchedly robbed of everything, had become as the poorest amongst people, and knew myself not how.

O eternal Error! I thought to myself, when will man tear himself free of your chains?

We speak of our heart, our plans, as though they were ours, and yet it is an unknown force that tosses us about and lays us in the grave as it pleases, and of which we know not from whence it comes nor whither it goes.

We want to grow up this way, and that way spread out our boughs and branches, and yet Earth and tempest takes us whither it lists, and when lightning strikes your crown and splits you down to your root, poor tree! what does it have to do with you?

Thus I thought. Are you annoyed by it, my Bellarmin! You will hear yet other things.

That exactly, dear one! is the tragedy, that our spirit so gladly assumes the appearance of the erring heart, so gladly fastens onto the fleeting sorrow, that the thought that should have healed the pain becomes ill itself, that the gardener so often tears his hand on the roses he should have planted, O! that has made many into a fool in front of others, whom otherwise, like an Orpheus, he could have ruled, that has so often made the noblest nature into a mockery for people as one finds on every street, that is the precipice for the favourites of Heaven, that their love is powerful and tender like their spirit, that the waves of the heart often move more powerfully and quickly than the trident with which the Sea God rules them, and therefore, dear one! let no man overreach himself!

HYPERION TO BELLARMIN

Can you bear to hear it, will you comprehend it, when I speak to you of my long sick grief?

Take me as I prove myself to be, and reflect that it is better to die, because one lived, than to live, because one has never lived! Do not envy those free of suffering, the wooden idols, for whom nothing is lacking because their soul is so poor, who ask naught of rain and sunshine because they have nothing that needs cultivation.

Yes! yes! it is very easy to be happy, calm, with a shallow heart and limited spirit. Begrudge you one cannot; for who gets excited because the wooden target does not lament when the arrow pierces it and the hollow vessel resounds so dully if someone throws it at the wall?

But you must moderate yourselves, dear people, must marvel in all quietness if you cannot understand that others are not so happy, or so self-sufficient, you must indeed check yourselves from making your prudence into law, for then it would be the end of the world if one obeyed you.

I lived now very quietly, very undemandingly in Tenos. I now really allowed the happenings of the world to pass by as mist in Autumn, laughed also occasionally with tearful eyes at my heart, when it flew forth, to sup like the bird to the painted grape, and remained thereby calm and friendly.

I now gladly allowed each his opinion, his ill breeding. I was converted, I no more desired to convert anyone, I was only sad when I saw that people believed I allowed their nonsense to go on without comment, because I regarded it as highly and dearly as they. I did not exactly want to surrender myself to their stupidities, yet I tried to be indulgent where I was able. Indeed, that is their pleasure, I thought, indeed they subsist on it!

Often I even consented to take part, and however soulless and unmotivated I was, it was noticed by none, no one missed anything, and if I had said they should forgive me, they would have stood there and wondered and asked: what then have you done to us? The indulgent ones!

Often, when in the morning I stood there by my window and the busy day met me, I could momentarily forget myself, could look around me as though I wanted to undertake something in which my being would still have taken delight as before, but then I scolded myself, then remembered, like one from whom a sound of his mother tongue escapes in a country where it is not understood — whither, my heart? I said rationally to myself and obeyed.

What is it then, that man desires so much? I often asked; what is the meaning then of the infinity in his breast? Infinity? where is it then? who then has perceived it? He desires more than he knows! that could be true! O! that you have experienced often enough. It is also as it should be. That gives the sweet, wildly enthusiastic feeling of power, that it does not issue forth as it desires, just that makes the beautiful dreams of immortality and all the lovely and the colossal phantoms that manifoldly charm the people, that creates for man his Elysium and his Gods, that his path in life does not run straight, that he does not go forth like an arrow, and a foreign power casts itself in the way of the fugitive.

The heart's wave would not surge up so wonderfully and become spirit if the ancient silent rock, Fate, did not confront it.

And yet the moving force within our breast dies, and with it our Gods and their Heaven.

The fire rises up in joyful forms, out of the dark cradle where it slept, and its flame climbs and falls, and becomes refracted and joyfully embraces itself again, until its substance is consumed, then it smokes and struggles and is extinguished; what remains, is ash.

Thus it is with us. That is the essence of everything that the wise, in terrible fascinating mysteries, relate to us. And you? what would you ask yourself? That then sometimes something in you flares up, and, like the mouth of the dying, your heart in *one* moment opens itself to you so powerfully and then locks itself away, just that is the ill omen.

Just be still and let it take its course! do not fabricate! do not childishly try to make yourself an ell greater than you are! — It is as though you want to create another Sun and new pupils for her, produce an Earth and a Moon.

Thus I dreamt away. Patiently I gradually took my leave of all. — Oh you colleagues of my time! question not your doctors and not the priests, if you inwardly are perishing!

You have lost the belief in all that is great; then must, then must you perish, if this belief does not return like a comet out of foreign Skies.

HYPERION TO BELLARMIN

There is a forgetting of all existence, a silencing of our being, where it is to us as though we had found everything.

There is a silencing, a forgetting of all existence, where it is to us as though we had lost everything, a night of our soul where no glimmer of a star, where not even a piece of rotten wood glows for us.

I had now become composed. Now nothing more started me up at midnight. No longer did I scorch myself in my own flame.

Now, quiet and solitary, I looked before me, and did not wander with my eye in the past and in the future. Now things far and near did not press themselves upon my senses; people, if they did not force me to see them, I saw not.

Formerly, this century had often lain before my senses like the ever empty vessel of the Danaides, and with lavish love my soul poured itself out, to fill the gaps; now I saw the gaps no more, now life's tediousness oppressed me no more.

Never now did I say to the flower, you are my sister! and to the Springs, we are of one kind! I now gave faithfully, like an echo, each thing its name.

Like a river between arid banks, where no willow leaf is reflected in the water, unbeautified, the world flowed past me.

HYPERION TO BELLARMIN

There is nothing that can grow and so profoundly perish as man. With the night of the abyss he often compares his suffering, and with the Aether his bliss, and how little is said thereby.

But there is nothing more beautiful than when after such a long death, it dawns again within him and pain, like a brother, goes to meet distantly dawning joy.

Oh, it was a divine intimation with which I now greeted the coming Spring again! Like the distant string-music of lovers in the silent air when all sleeps, so its soft melodies sounded about my breast; as though across from Elysium, I sensed its coming, when the dead branches moved and a soft breeze touched my cheek.

Lovely Sky of Ionia! never had I clung to you in such a way, but neither had my heart been so similar to you as then, in its bright loving play. —

Who does not yearn for the joys of love and great deeds when in the eye of Heaven and in the bosom of the Earth, Spring returns?

I arose as from a sick bed, gently and slowly, but with secret hopes my breast trembled so blissfully that I thereby forgot to ask what this meant.

More beautiful dreams embraced me now in sleep, and when I awoke they remained in my heart like the trace of a kiss on the cheek of the lover. Oh, the morning light and I, we met each other now like reconciled friends when, though still a little distant, they carry in their souls the imminent eternal moment of embrace.

My eye now really opened once again, certainly no longer as before, armed and full of inherent strength; it had become more beseeching, it implored for life and yet in my depths it was as though it could be with me again as before, and better.

I looked at people again as though also I ought to be active and enjoy myself amongst them. With real affection I joined in everywhere.

Heavens! what a malicious joy that was, to see the proud odd person now for once become one of them! What a joke they found it that hunger had driven the deer of the forest to run into their poultry yard! —

Ah! my Adamas I sought, my Alabanda, but there appeared to me neither.

Finally I also wrote to Smyrna, and as I wrote it was as though all lovingness and all power of the man were concentrated into One moment when I wrote; thus I wrote three times, but no answer, I beseeched, I threatened, reminded of all the hours of love and boldness, but no answer from the unforgettable one, loved unto death — Alabanda! I cried, O my Alabanda! you have condemned me to death. You held me still upright, were the last hope of my youth! Now I want nothing more! Now it is final!

We pity the dead as though they felt death, and yet the dead have peace. But that, that is pain which is unequalled, that is an unceasing feeling of absolute annihilation, when our life so loses its meaning, when the heart says to itself, you must go down and nothing of you remains; no flower have you planted, built no hut, so that you might at least say: I leave a trace behind on Earth. Alas! and the soul can ever be so full of yearning for all that it is despondent!

I sought continually for something, but I did not dare to open my eyes before people. I had times when I dreaded the laughter of a child.

But thereby I was mostly very quiet and patient, had also often a wonderful superstition about the healing power of some things; from a dove that I bought, a boat journey, a valley that the mountains hid from me, I could find comfort.

Enough! enough! had I grown up with Themistocles, had I lived amongst the Scipiones, my soul would truly never have known itself from this side.

HYPERION TO BELLARMIN

Occasionally some power of the spirit still moved in me. But, indeed, only destructively.

What is man? I could begin; how is it, that there is such a thing in the world that, like a chaos, ferments, or moulders, like a rotten tree, and never develops to maturity? How can Nature tolerate this unripe grape amongst her sweet grapes?

To the plants he says, I was once also, like you! and to the pure Stars, I will become, like you, in another world! meanwhile he dissects and practises now and then his arts on himself as though, when it is finally unravelled, he could put the living together again like masonry; but it does not disconcert him if nothing is bettered by all his doings; what he does still always remains a trick.

O you poor ones, you who feel this, you who also do not like to speak of human purpose, you who also are so thoroughly affected by the Nothing that holds its sway over us, who see so clearly that we are born for Nothing, that we love a Nothing, believe in Nothing, overwork ourselves for Nothing in order to gradually change into Nothing — what can I do if you break down when you seriously reflect on it? Have I indeed not also sometimes sunk down into these thoughts, and cried, why do you put the axe to my roots, terrible Spirit? and am still here.

Oh once, you dark brothers! it was otherwise. Then above us it was so beautiful, so beautiful and happy before us; these hearts also flowed over before the distant blessèd phantoms, and, boldly triumphant, our spirits also penetrated upwards and broke through the bounds, and as they looked around, woe, there was an infinite emptiness.

O! I can throw myself on my knees and wring my hands and implore, I know not whom?, for other thoughts. But I cannot over-come it, the glaring truth. Have I not twofold convinced myself? When I look at life, what is the end of all? Nothing. When I ascend in spirit, what is the highest of all? Nothing.

But quiet, my heart! For it is the last of your strength you squander! the last of your strength? and you, you want to storm the Heavens? where then are your hundred arms, Titan, where your Pelion and Ossa, your steps to the citadel of the father of the Gods so that you climb up and cast down the God and his Table of the Gods and all the immortal peaks of Olympus and preach to the mortals: stay below, children of the moment! strive not to these heights for there is nothing here above.

You can desist from seeing that which holds sway over others. For you is valid your new teaching. Above you and before you it is indeed empty and barren because within you it is empty and barren.

Indeed, if you are richer than I, you others, you could probably help a little.

If your garden is so full of flowers, why does their breath not delight me as well? — If you are so full of the Divine, then offer it to me to drink. For no one suffers want at festivals, not even the poorest. But One only holds his festival amongst you; that is Death.

Want and Fear and Night are your masters. They divide you, they drive you together with blows. Hunger you call Love, and where you see nothing more, there live your gods. Gods and Love?

Oh, the poets are right, there is nothing so small and insignificant that cannot inspire one.

Thus I thought. How that all came to me. I yet cannot grasp.

SECOND BOOK

HYPERION TO BELLARMIN

I am now living on the island of Ajax, dear Salamis.

I love all of this Greece. It bears the colour of my heart. Wherever one looks, lies a buried joy.

And yet there is also so much around one that is dear and great.

On the headland I have built myself a hut of mastic branches, and planted around moss and trees and thyme and all sorts of bushes.

There I have my dearest hours, there I sit evenings long and look across to Attica, until finally my heart beats too much; then I take my tackle, go down to the bay and catch fish for myself.

Or I read up there on my heights of the old glorious sea battle that raged off Salamis in wisely governed tumult, and rejoice in the spirit that could direct and restrain the furious chaos of friends and foes, like a rider his steed, and am most fervently ashamed of my own war history.

Or I gaze out to the sea and reflect on my life, its ascent and fall, its bliss and its grief and my past sounds to me often like a lyre where the master runs through all the tones and throws together discord and harmony with hidden order.

Today it is thrice as beautiful up here. Two friendly days of rain have cooled the air and the weary Earth.

The ground has become greener, the field more open. Infinite there, stands the golden corn mixed with the joyful cornflower and, luminous and clear, a thousand hopeful peaks climb out of the depths of the wood. Delicate and great, each distant lineament wanders through space; like steps, the mountains rise up to the Sun unceasingly one after another. The whole sky is pure. The white light is only breathed over the Aether, and in the bright day, like a little silver cloud, the shy moon floats by.

HYPERION TO BELLARMIN

For a long time it has not been with me, as now.

Like Jupiter's eagle to the song of the Muses, I harken to the wonderful infinite harmony in me. Unassailed in mind and soul, strong and joyful, with smiling seriousness, I play in spirit with Fortune and the three sisters, the holy Fates. Full of divine youth my whole being exults in itself, in everything. Like the starry Heavens I am silent and moved.

I have long awaited such a festival, to be able to write to you once more. Now I am strong enough; now let me tell you.

In the midst of my dark days an acquaintance from Calaurea invited me over. I should come to his mountains, he wrote to me; one lived there more freely than elsewhere and also there blossomed in the midst of the pine woods and rapid waters, lemon groves and palms and lovely herbs and myrtles and the holy vine. A garden he had made high in the mountains and a house; dense trees shaded it at the back and cooling breezes played softly around it in the burning Summer days; like a bird at the top of a cedar, one looked down into the depths, to the villages and green hills and contented homes of the island, that all, like children, lay around the glorious mountain and nourished themselves from its foaming brooks.

That indeed roused me then a little. It was a clear blue April day, on which I took the ship across. The sea was unusually beautiful and pure, and light the Air, as in higher regions. In the airily floating ship one left the Earth behind like an excellent meal when the holy wine is served.

My gloomy mind struggled in vain against the influence of the Sea and Air. I surrendered, asked nothing of myself and others, sought nothing, reflected on nothing, let myself be rocked into half-sleep by the boat, and imagined to myself I lay in Charon's skiff. O, it is sweet, thus to drink from the cup of forgetfulness.

My jovial sailor would have gladly spoken with me but I was very taciturn.

He pointed with his finger and showed me to the right and left the blue island, but I did not look for long, and was in the next moment once more in my own dear dreams.

Finally, when he showed me the peaceful peaks in the distance and said we should soon be in Calaurea, I took more notice, and my whole being opened itself to the wonderful power that all at once, sweetly and quietly and inexplicably played with me. Wide-eyed, amazed and joyful, I looked out into the mysteries of the distance, lightly trembled my heart and in friendly haste I involuntarily grasped my sailor — so? I cried, that is Calaurea? And in the way he then looked at me, I myself did not know what to make of myself. I greeted my friend with wonderful tenderness. Full of sweet unrest was my whole being.

In the afternoon I wanted to immediately roam round part of the island. The woods and mysterious valleys enticed me indescribably and the friendly day charmed everything forth.

It was so apparent how every living thing desired more than daily food, how also the bird has its festival and the animal.

It was delightful to regard. As when the mother caressingly asks where around her is her dearest, and all children rush into her lap and the smallest also stretches its arms from the cradle, so flew and leapt and strove all life out into the divine Air, and beetles and swallows and doves and storks tumbled amongst one another in exultant confusion in the depths and the heights, and that which the Earth bound, their steps became flight, the horse stormed over the ditches and over the hedges the deer, and from the seabed the fish came up and skipped over the surface. The maternal Air penetrated to the heart of everything and lifted it and drew it to her.

And the people went out of their doors and felt wonderfully the moving spirit, how it gently moved the fine hair over their brow, how it cooled the light's ray and friendly loosed their garments for them to take it to their breast, breathed more sweetly, touched more tenderly the light clear caressing Sea, by which they lived and had their being.

O Sister of the Spirit, who, ardently powerful, rules and lives in us, holy Air! how lovely it is that, wherever I wander, you accompany me, omnipresent immortal one!

With the children the great element played most beautifully.

One hummed peacefully to itself, from one a rhythmless little song escaped his lips, from another a full-throated rejoicing; that one stretched, that one jumped in the air; another strolled about deep in thought.

And all this was the language of One well-being, all One response to the caresses of the enchanting Airs.

I was full of indescribable longing and peace. A strange power governed me. Friendly Spirit, I said to myself, whither are you calling me? to Elysium or whither?

I went into a wood by the purling water, up to where it trickled down over rocks, where, innocently, it glided over the pebbles and gradually narrowed, and the valley became a colonnade, and, lonely, the light of midday played in the silent darkness —

Here — I would like to be able to speak, my Bellarmin! Would gladly write to you calmly.

Speak? Oh, I am a layman of joy, I will speak!

Yet tranquillity dwells in the Land of the Blessèd, and beyond the Stars the heart forgets its distress and its language.

I have sacredly kept it! like a Palladium, I have carried it within me, the Divinity that appeared to me! and when henceforth Fate seizes me and casts me from one abyss to another, and all powers drown in me and all thoughts, so shall this Peerlessness still survive in me, and shine in me and rule in eternal indestructible clarity! —

Thus you lay poured forth, sweet life, thus you looked up, arose, stood there then, in slender fullness, divinely calm, and your heavenly face still full of the serene rapture in which I disturbed you.

O he who has looked into the calm of these eyes, he to whom these sweet lips have opened, of what else may he speak?

Peace of Beauty! divine Peace! he who once in you has assuaged the raging life and the doubting spirit, how can anything else help him?

I cannot speak of her, but there are times, when the best and the most beautiful appears as in clouds, and the Heaven of Perfection reveals itself to divining Love, then, Bellarmin! then remember her being! then bend your knee with me, and remember my bliss! but do not forget that I had what you sense, that I, with these eyes, saw what to you appears only as in clouds.

That people sometimes like to say: they rejoiced! O believe, you have not yet an inkling of what joy is! To you the shadow of its shadow has not yet appeared! O go, and speak not of the blue Aether, you blind ones!

That one can become like the children, that once more the golden time of innocence returns, the time of peace and freedom, so that there is just One joy, One resting place on Earth!

Is man not agèd, faded, is he not like a fallen leaf that cannot find its branch again and then is chased about by the winds until the sand buries it?

And yet his Spring returns again!

Weep not if the most excellent withers! soon it will grow young again! Mourn not if your heart's melody becomes silent! soon a hand will be there again to tune it!

How then was I! was I not like a broken lyre? A few tones I had, but they were the tones of death. I had sung myself a mournful swan song! I would have gladly wound myself a funeral wreath, but I had only Winter flowers.

And where were they then now, the deathly silence, the night and desert of my life? the whole sorry mortality?

Truly, life is poor and lonely. We live down here like the diamond in the shaft. We ask in vain how we came down here, in order to find the way up again.

We are like fire that sleeps in the dry branch or in the pebble; and struggle and seek in each moment the end of the confined imprisonment. But they will come, outweighing aeons of struggle, the moments of release, when the Divine will burst open the prison, when the flame frees itself from the wood and triumphantly soars up over the ashes, ha! it will be to us as though the unchained spirit, forgetting the suffering, the subjugation, were returning in triumph back to the Halls of the Sun.

HYPERION TO BELLARMIN

I was once happy, Bellarmin! Am I still? Would I not be, even if the holy moment, when I saw her for the first time, had been my last?

I have Once seen it, the Peerless One, that my soul sought, and the perfection that we place up beyond the stars, that we put off to the end of Time, that I have actually felt. It was there, the Highest, in this realm of human nature and matter, it was there!

I ask no more, where it is; it was in the world, it can return to it, it is now just more concealed in it. I ask no more, what it is; I have seen it, I have known it.

O ye who seek the highest and the best in the depths of knowledge, in the turmoil of commerce, in the dark of the past, in the labyrinth of the future, in the tombs or beyond the stars! do you know its name? the name of that which is One and All?

Its name is Beauty.

Did you know what you desired? I still do not know, yet I have a presentiment of it, the New Divinity's new Realm, and I hasten towards it and seize the others and lead them with me as the river takes the rivers into the ocean.

And you, you have shown me the way! With you I began. They are not worth the words, the days when I did not know you —

O, Diotima, Diotima, heavenly being!

HYPERION TO BELLARMIN

Let us forget that Time exists and count not the days of life!

What are centuries compared with the moment, when two beings thus have a divination of one another and draw near?

I still see the evening, on which Notara for the first time took me to her in her house.

She dwelt only a few hundred steps from us at the foot of the mountain.

Her mother was a thinking sensitive being, a simple joyful youth the brother, and both affectionately admitted that in all things Diotima was queen of the household.

Ah! everything was hallowed, beautified by her presence. Wherever I looked, whatever I touched, her carpet, her cushion, her little table, everything was in secret union with her. And when she for the first time called me by name, when she herself came so close to me that her innocent breath touched my harkening being! —

We spoke very little with one another. One was ashamed of speech. One would have liked to become a tone and unite in One Heavenly Song.

Of what also should we speak? We saw only each other. To speak of ourselves, we were shy.

Of the life of the Earth we spoke finally.

So ardently and childlike no hymn has yet been sung to her.

It did us good, to strew the abundance of our souls into the lap of the good Mother. We felt ourselves thereby eased, like the trees, when the Summer wind shakes the fruitful branches, and showers their sweet apples into the grass.

We called the Earth one of the flowers of the Aether and the Aether we called the infinite Garden of Life. As the roses rejoice in golden pollen, we said, so the heroic Sunlight delights the Earth with his beams; she is a glorious living being, we said, equally divine, whether wrathful fire or mild clear water springs from her heart, always happy whether she lives on dew drops or storm clouds, which she, for pleasure, prepares for herself with the help of the Aether, she, the ever faithful loving half of the Sun God, perhaps more intimately united with him, but then through a supreme Fate separated from him, so that she must seek him, draw near to him, distance herself from him, and with joy and mourning ripen to the highest beauty.

Thus we spoke. I give you the content, the spirit of it. But what is it without the life?

It grew dusk, and we had to go. Good Night, you angel eyes! I thought in my heart, and may you again soon appear to me, beautiful, divine spirit, with your peace and plenty!

HYPERION TO BELLARMIN

A few days later they came up to us. We walked about together in the garden. Diotima and I got ahead, absorbed; often my eyes filled with tears of rapture over the saintly one who so unassumingly walked by my side.

We now stood at the edge of the mountain-top and looked out into the unending East.

Diotima's eyes opened wide and quietly, as a bud opens, her dear little face opened before the airs of Heaven, became pure speech and soul and, as though she began a flight into the clouds, her whole form stood stretched gently upwards in easy majesty, her feet hardly touching the Earth.

O, how I would have liked to grasp her under the arms, like the eagle his Ganymede, and fly thence with her over the Sea and its islands.

Now she stepped further forward and looked down the sheer cliff face. She liked to survey the terrifying depth and to lose herself down into the night of the forests which beneath, through rocks and foaming streams, stretched up their bright tree tops.

The parapet on which she supported herself was somewhat low. So I had to hold her a little, the charming one, while she thus bent forward. Ah! hot trembling joy coursed through my being and wild transport was in all my senses and my hands burnt me like coals when I touched her.

And then the heart's delight, to stand so intimately next to her, and the tender, childlike care that she might fall, and the joy at the enthusiasm of the glorious maiden!

What is all, that in thousands of years man did and thought compared with One moment of love? For it is also the most successful, the most divine beauty in Nature! thither lead all steps from the threshold of life. Thence we come, thither we go.

HYPERION TO BELLARMIN

That I should only forget her song! that only these soul tones should never return into my unceasing dreams!

One does not know the proudly floating swan when, sleeping, he sits on the bank.

Only when she sang, one recognised the dear silent one who so unwillingly consented to speech.

Then, only then, the divinely disobliging one arose in her majesty and loveliness; then it often drifted so pleadingly und so caressingly, often like a prayer to the Gods, from the tenderly blossoming lips. And how the heart moved in this divine voice, how all greatness and humility, all joy and all mourning of life appeared beautified in the nobility of these tones!

As in flight the swallow seizes the bees, so always she touched us all.

Not joy or admiration came amongst us, but the peace of Heaven.

A thousand times I have said to her and to myself: the most beautiful is also the most holy. And thus was everything with her. As her song, so also her life.

HYPERION TO BELLARMIN

Amongst the flowers her heart was at home, as though it were one of them.

She called them all by name, out of love created new, more beautiful ones for them and knew exactly the happiest life time of each.

Like a sister, when from every corner a loved one comes to her and each one would dearly like to be the first to be greeted, so was the quiet being busy with eye and hand, spiritually preoccupied, when in the meadow we walked, or in the wood.

And that was so absolutely not assumed, taught, thus had it grown up with her.

It is eternally true and everywhere apparent: the more innocent, more beautiful a soul, the more intimate with the other happy lives that are called soulless.

HYPERION TO BELLARMIN

A thousand times I have in my heart's joy laughed at those people who imagine that a noble spirit cannot possibly know how to prepare vegetables. Diotima could very well, at the right time, speak most heartily of the hearth, and there is certainly nothing nobler than a noble maiden who tends the all-beneficent flame and, similar to Nature, prepares a heart-gladdening meal.

HYPERION TO BELLARMIN

What is all the artificial knowledge in the world, what is the proud majority of human thoughts against the unsought tones of this spirit that did not know what it knew, what it was?

Who would not prefer the grape full and fresh, just as it has sprung from the root, to the dried picked berry, that the merchant presses into the crate and sends into the world? What is the wisdom of a book against the wisdom of an angel?

She always appeared to say so little, and said so much.

I accompanied her home once in the late gloaming; like dreams, bedewed clouds stole over the meadow, like harkening Geniuses the blessèd Stars looked through the branches.

One seldom heard a 'how lovely!' from her mouth, even though her innocent heart left no whispering leaf, no trickling Spring unheard.

This time, however, she uttered it to me — how beautiful!

It is probably thus to please us! I said rather like children that say something neither in jest nor earnest.

I can well imagine what you say, she replied; I like best to think of the world as a domestic life where everything, without actually thinking about it, fits in with one another, and where one lives for the pleasure and joy of each other, purely because it comes from the heart.

Joyful sublime belief! I cried.

She was silent for a while.

Also we then, are children of the house, I finally began again, are and will be.

Will be eternally, she responded.

Will we be? I asked.

I trust, she continued, Nature in this as I trust her daily.

O I would have liked to have been Diotima, when she said that! But you do not know what she said, my Bellarmin. You have not seen it and not heard.

You are right, I cried to her; the eternal Beauty, Nature, suffers no loss just as she suffers no addition. Her adornment is tomorrow other than it was today; but our best, us, us she cannot do without and you least of all. We believe that we are eternal because our soul feels the Beauty of Nature. She is an imperfect work, is not the divine, the perfect, if ever you were missing from her. She does not deserve your heart if she has to blush at your hopes.

HYPERION TO BELLARMIN

So free from wants, so divinely sufficient I have never known anything.

Like the wave of the ocean around the shore of the Blessèd Isles, so my restless heart flowed round the peace of the heavenly maiden.

I had nothing to give her but a soul full of wild contradictions, full of bleeding memories, nothing I had to give her but my boundless love with its thousand cares, its thousand raging hopes; but she stood there before me in unchanging beauty, untroubled, in smiling perfection, and all yearning, all dreams of mortality, ah! all that in the golden hours of morning the Genius prophesies of higher realms, it was all fulfilled in this one quiet soul.

One usually says that beyond the Stars the struggle will fade away, only in the time to come, it is promised us, when our yeast has sunk down will our fermenting life be changed into noble joyous wine, the heart's peace of the Blessèd can be sought nowhere else on this Earth. I know otherwise. I have come the nearer way. I stood before her, and heard and saw the peace of Heaven, and in the midst of sighing chaos there appeared to me Urania.

How often have I stilled my laments before this image! how often has the wild life and the striving spirit calmed down when, rapt in blessèd contemplation, I looked into her heart as one looks into the Spring, when it is quietly quivering from the touch of Heaven that in silver drops falls onto it!

She was my Lethe, this soul, my holy Lethe, from which I drank the forgetfulness of being so that I stood before her like an immortal, and joyfully scolded myself and, as after oppressive dreams, had to smile at all chains which had oppressed me.

O I would have become a happy, an excellent person with her!

With her! but that has turned out ill, and I now wander about in that which is before and in me and beyond, and know not what to make of myself and other things.

My soul is like a fish cast out of its element onto the sands of the shore, and writhes and throws itself about, until it withers in the heat of the day.

Ah! if only there were still something in the world for me to do! if only there were work, a war for me, that would refresh me!

A little boy that had been torn from the mothers' breast and thrown into the desert, was once, so it is said, suckled by a vixen.

My heart is not so fortunate!

HYPERION TO BELLARMIN

I can only here and there speak a little word of her. I must forget what she wholly is if I am to speak of her. I must deceive myself, as though she had lived in former times, as though I knew a little about her through stories, if her living image is not to seize me so that I pine away in ecstasy and pain, if, in the death of joy in her, and the death of mourning for her, I am not to die.

HYPERION TO BELLARMIN

It is in vain; I cannot hide it from myself. Wherever I flee with my thoughts, up into the Heavens, and into the abyss, to the beginning and to the end of time, even when He who was my last refuge, who once consumed every care in me, who once burnt up every joy and every pain of life in his flame of fire, in which He reveals himself, even when I throw myself into his arms, the glorious, mysterious Spirit of the World, dive down into his depths, as into the bottomless ocean, even there, the sweet terror finds me out, the sweet, bewildering, killing terror that Diotima's grave is near me.

Do you hear? do you hear? Diotima's grave!

Yet though, my heart had become so quiet and my love was buried with the dead whom I loved.

You know, my Bellarmin! for a long time I did not write to you about her and when I did write, I think I wrote calmly.

What is it then now?

I go out to the shore and look over to Calaurea, where she rests, that is it.

O that no one lends me a little boat, that no one is moved to pity and offers me his oar and helps me over to her!

May indeed the good Sea not stay calm, so that I may not cut myself a piece of wood and swim over to her.

But I will throw myself into the raging Sea, and ask its waves to throw me on to Diotima's shore! —

Dear brother! I comfort my heart with all sorts of phantasies, I offer myself many a sleeping draught; and it would indeed be greater to free one's self for ever than to help one's self with palliatives; but with whom is it not so? I am with that then satisfied.

Satisfied? ah that would be good! that would have helped where no God can help.

Now! now! I have done what I could. I demand from Fate my soul.

HYPERION TO BELLARMIN

Was she not mine, you Sisters of Fate, was she not mine? The pure Springs I call upon as witnesses, and the innocent trees that harkened to us, and the daylight and the Aether! was she not mine? united with me in all tones of life?

Where is the being that like mine, recognised her? in which mirror were concentrated as in me, the beams of this light? was she not joyfully startled at her own glory when she first became aware of it in my joy? Ah! where is the heart, that like mine, was at all times so close to her, fulfilled her and was by her fulfilled, that was so solely there to embrace her, as the eyelash is there for the eye.

We were just one flower, and our souls lived in each other as the flower when she loves and hides her tender joy in the closed calyx.

And yet, yet, like a usurped crown, she was torn from me and laid in the dust.

HYPERION TO BELLARMIN

Before either of us knew it, we belonged to each other.

When I thus, with all homage of my heart, so spiritually over-come, stood before her and was silent and all my life surrendered itself to the beams of the eye that saw only her, embraced only her, and she then in return, tenderly hesitating, regarded me, and did not know where I was with my thoughts; when often I espied her joyfully and beautifully immersed in a charming task, and at the slightest movement like the bee round the slender branch, my soul wandered and flew, and when she then, in peaceful thoughts, turned to me and, surprised at my joy, my joy would have to hide itself, and at the dear work again sought her peace and found —

When she, wonderfully all-knowing, revealed to me each harmony, each dissonance in the depth of my being the moment it began, before even I myself became aware of it, when she saw each shadow of a little cloud on the brow, each shadow of sadness, of pride on the lips, each spark in the eye, when she overheard the ebb and flow of my heart, and, full of care, anticipated gloomy hours, whilst my spirit, too intemperate, too extravagant, consumed itself in exuberant talk, when the dear being, truer than a mirror, revealed to me each change of my cheek and often in friendly solicitudes about my unsteady nature, admonished me, and chastised like a dear child —

Ah! when you once, innocent one, counted on your fingers the steps down from our mountain to your house, when you showed me your walks, the places where you had formerly sat and related to me how you had passed the time there, and finally said to me it now seemed to you as though I also had always been there —

Had we not then long since belonged to each other?

HYPERION TO BELLARMIN

I build my heart a tomb that it may rest; I spin myself a cocoon because everywhere it is Winter; in blessèd memories I wrap myself up against the storm.

We sat once with Notara — thus was the friend called with whom I lived — and a few others who like ourselves also belonged to the originals of Calaurea, in Diotima's garden, under blossoming almond trees and spoke, amongst other things, of friendship.

I had taken little part, for some time I had kept myself from talking too much about things that were close to the heart, my Diotima had made me so taciturn —

When Harmodius and Aristogiton lived, cried one finally, then there was still friendship in the world. That delighted me too much to be able to keep silent.

A crown should be plaited for you for those words! I called to him; have you then really an inkling of it, have you a comparison for the friendship of Aristogiton and Harmodius? Forgive me! But by Aether! one must be Aristogiton to be able to feel how Aristogiton lived, and indeed the lightning may not be feared by the man who would wish to be loved with Harmodius' love for I am deceived in all things, if the terrible youth did not love with the severity of Minos. Few have come through such a trial, and it is no easier to be a Demigod's friend than to sit at the table of the Gods like Tantalus. But there is also nothing more glorious on Earth than when a proud pair as this is so mutually submissive.

That is also my hope, my desire in lonely hours, that such great tones and greater must one day return into the symphony of the world's course. Love gave birth to centuries full of vivid men; friendship will bear them again. From infant harmony nations once arose, the harmony of spirits will be the beginning of a new world history. From seedling joy mankind began and grew up, and grew, until it ripened; from then on it increasingly fermented from within and without, until now the human race, infinitely decomposed, lies there like a chaos, so that all who still feel and see, are seized with dizziness; but Beauty flees from the life of man up into the Spirit; Ideal will be what Nature was, and if the base of the tree is withered and weather-beaten, there has still arisen out of it a new crown, and gleams green in the Sun, as did once the trunk in the days of youth; Ideal is what Nature was. In this, in this ideal, this rejuvenated divinity, the few recognise themselves and they are One, for it is One in them, and from this, this, begins the Second Age of the world — I have said enough to make clear what I think.

You should have seen Diotima, how she sprang up and gave me both her hands and cried: I have understood it, dear one, completely understood, so much it says.

Love gave birth to the world, friendship will bear it again.

O then, you future ones, you new Dioscuri, then tarry awhile when you pass by, there where Hyperion sleeps, tarry foreseeing over the forgotten man's ashes, and say: he would have been as one of us, were he now here.

That I have heard, my Bellarmin! that I have experienced, and go not willingly unto death?

Yes! yes! I have been paid in advance, I have lived. More joy could a God bear, but not I.

HYPERION TO BELLARMIN

Would you ask how it was with me at this time? As one who had lost everything to win everything.

Often, I confess, I came from Diotima's trees like one elated with victory, often I had to hurry away from her, so that I did not betray my thoughts to anyone; joy so raged in me, and pride, the all-inspiring belief, to be loved by Diotima.

Then I sought out for myself the highest mountain and its Airs, and like an eagle, for whom his bleeding pinion is healed, my Spirit stirred in the open-air, and spread, as though it were his, over the manifest world; wonderful! it was often to me as though the things of the Earth refined themselves and melted together like gold in my fire, and from them and me a divinity arose, joy so raged in me; and how I lifted up the children and pressed them to my beating heart, how I greeted the plants and the trees! I would have liked to wish for myself a spell to bring the shy deer and all the wild birds of the forest like a domestic tribe around my generous hands, so blissfully foolish did I love everything!

But not long, then all that, like a light was extinguished in me, and silent and melancholy like a shadow, I sat there and sought for the vanished life. Complain I did not want to, and to comfort myself I also did not want. Hope I threw away, like a cripple, for whom the crutch is spoiled; I was ashamed of weeping; I was ashamed of existing at all. But finally then pride broke out into tears, and the suffering, that I would have gladly denied, became dear to me, and I laid it like a child to my breast.

No, cried my heart, no, my Diotima! it pains not. Preserve your peace for yourself and let me go my way. Do not let your calm be disturbed, lovely star! if beneath you all is in ferment and clouded.

O do not allow your rose to fade, blessèd child of the Gods! Let not your beauty age in the cares of the world. For that is my joy, sweet life! that you carry within you carefree Heaven. You must not become needy, no, no! you must not see in yourself the poverty of love.

And when I then went down to her again — I would have liked to ask the little breeze and perceive in the course of clouds, how it would be with me in an hour! and how it delighted me when any friendly face met me on the way, and just not too drily called out to me his 'Good day'!

When a little girl came out of the wood and offered me a bouquet of strawberries for sale, with an expression that she would like to give it to me, or when a peasant where I passed by, sat gathering in his cherry tree, and called down to me from the branches whether I would not like to taste a handful; those were good signs for the superstitious heart!

If one of Diotima's windows stood wide open towards the path down which I came, how pleasing that could be!

She had perhaps not long since looked out of it.

And then I stood before her, breathless and hesitant, and pressed my entwined arms against my heart, not to feel its trembling, and, like the swimmer out of the rapid waters, my spirit fought and strove not to drown in the unending love.

Of what should we speak at the moment? I could cry, one often has difficulty, one cannot find material on which to fasten one's thoughts.

Do they pull you out again into the air? replied my Diotima. You must bind lead to their wings, or I will tie a thread to them like the boy to the flying dragon, so that they do not escape from us.

The dear girl tried to help herself and me with a jest, but little came of it.

Yes, yes! I cried, as you like, as you think best — shall I read aloud? Your lute is probably still tuned from yesterday — also I have not anything to read aloud just now —

You have already promised more than once, she said, to tell me how you lived before we knew one another, would you not like to now?

That is true, I replied; my heart threw itself gladly into it, and I then related to her, as to you, of Adamas and my lonely days in Smyrna, of Alabanda and how I became separated from him, and of the inexplicable malady of my being, before I came over to Calaurea — now you know all, I said to her calmly, when I came to the end, now you will take less offence at me; now you will say, I added smiling, mock not this Vulcan if he limps, for twice have the Gods thrown him from Heaven to Earth.

Hush, cried she with stifled voice, and hid her tears in her handkerchief, O hush, and do not jest about your fate, about your heart! for I understand it, and better than you.

Dear — dear Hyperion! It is indeed very difficult to help you.

Do you know then, she continued with heightened voice, do you know then of what you are in want, the one thing that is missing for you, what you, like Alpheus his Arethusa, are seeking, over that which you are mourning in all your mourning? It is not just years ago it departed, one cannot exactly say when it was, when it went away, but it was, it is, in you it is! It is a better time, that you seek, a more beautiful world. Only this world you embraced in your friends, with them you became this world.

In Adamas it rose for you; it also departed with him. In Alabanda the light appeared to you for the second time, but more ardent and passionate, and therefore it was also like a midnight of your soul when, for you he was gone.

Do you now also see, why the smallest doubt about Alabanda was bound to become despair in you? why you cast him off, only because he was not a God?

You did not want a man, believe me, you wanted a world. The loss of all the golden centuries, as you experienced them, concentrated into One joyful moment, the Spirit of all Spirits of a better time, the strength of all strength of the Heroes, this should one individual, one person replace! — Do you now see how poor, how rich you are? why you should be so proud, and also so cast down? why so terribly joy and suffering alternate for you?

For this reason, because you have everything and nothing, because the phantom of the golden days, that should come, belongs to you, and yet is not there, because you are a citizen in the regions of justice and beauty, are a god amongst Gods in the beautiful dreams that steal upon you by day, and when you awake, stand on modern Greek soil.

Twice, you say? O in one day you will be thrown seventy times from Heaven to Earth. Shall I tell you? I fear for you, you endure with difficulty the fate of these times. You will still try many a thing, will —

O God! and your final refuge will be a grave.

No, Diotima, I cried, no, by Heaven, no! As long as One melody sounds to me, I do not shun the deathly stillness of the wilderness beneath the Stars; as long as the Sun only shines and Diotima, no night exists for me.

Let the death knell toll for all the Virtues! I hear but you, you, the song of your heart, you, Belovèd! and find immortal life, whilst all becomes extinguished and fades away.

O Hyperion, she cried, what are you saying?

"I speak as I must. I can not, can no longer hide all the blessed-ness and fear and grief — Diotima! — Yes you know it, must know it, have seen it for a long time, that I am lost, if you do not offer me your hand."

She was confounded, confused.

And with me, with me will Hyperion stay? yes I wish it, now for the first time I wish, to be more than just a mortal girl. But I am to you what I can be.

O then you are everything to me, I cried!

"Everything, naughty hypocrite! and mankind that you yet purpose to solely love?"

Mankind? said I; I would that mankind would make Diotima a watchword and paint your image on its standards and say: today shall the Divine be victorious! Angel of Heaven, that would be a day!

Go, she cried, go, and show Heaven your transfiguration, it should not be so close to me.

You will go, will you not, dear Hyperion?

I obeyed. Who would not have obeyed? I went. Thus, I had never ever left her. O Bellarmin! that was joy, calm of life, peace of Gods, heavenly, wonderful, unrecognisable joy.

Words are here in vain, and he who asks for a comparison for her, he has not experienced her. The one thing that could express such a joy was Diotima's song when it hovered in the golden mean between height and depth.

O you willow banks of Lethe! you sunset glowing paths in Elysium's woods! you lilies by the streams of the valley! you rose wreaths of the hills! I believe in you, in this friendly hour, and say to my heart: there you will find her again, and all joy that you lost.

HYPERION TO BELLARMIN

I will relate to you more and more of my bliss.

I will put my breast to the test of the joys of the past until it becomes like steel, I will exercise myself in them until I am invincible.

Ha! but for all that they often fall like a sword stroke on my soul, but I play with the sword until I am accustomed to it, I hold my hand in the fire until I bear it like water.

I will not be faint hearted; yes! I will be strong! I will hide nothing from myself, will of all bliss conjure up from the grave the most blissful.

It is unbelievable that man should be fearful of the most beautiful; but it is so.

O indeed, a hundred times have I flown from these moments, this killing rapture of my memories and have turned my eye away like a child from lightning! and yet there grows in the luxuriant garden of the world nothing dearer than my joys, yet there thrives in Heaven and on Earth nothing nobler than my joys.

But only you, my Bellarmin, only a pure free soul as yours, do I tell it to. So liberal, as the Sun with its beams, I will not be; my pearls I will not throw before the foolish mass.

With each day since the last soul-conversation I knew myself less. I felt there was a holy secret between myself and Diotima.

I marvelled, dreamt. As though at midnight a blessèd spirit had appeared to me and chosen me to accompany him, thus it was in my soul.

O it is a strange mixture of bliss and melancholy when it is thus revealed, that we are forever out of our ordinary existence.

I had never since then managed to see Diotima alone. Always a third had to disturb us, part us, and the world lay between her and me like an unending void. Six terrifying days thus went by without my knowing anything of Diotima. It was as though the others around us paralysed my senses, as though they killed my whole outer life so that in no way the hidden soul could help itself over to her.

If I wanted to seek her with my eye, then before me it became night, if I wanted to turn to her with a little word, then it stuck in my throat.

Ah! the holy nameless yearning often wanted to rent my breast asunder, and the powerful love often raged like an imprisoned Titan in me. So deeply, so inwardly unreconciled had my spirit until now never striven against the chains that Fate forged for it, against the iron inexorable law to be separated, not to be One soul with one's other amiable half.

The star-bright night had now become my element. Then, when it was still as in the depths of the Earth where secretly the gold grows, then the more beautiful life of my love began.

Then the heart practised its right to invent. Then it told me how in Pre-Elysium, before he had come down to Earth, Hyperion's soul had played with his Diotima in divine childhood by the melodious sounds of the Spring, and beneath branches, as we see the branches on Earth when, beautified, they gleam out of the golden stream.

And like the Past, the gate of the Future opened itself in me.

There we flew, Diotima and I, there we migrated like swallows, from one Spring of the world to the next, through the Sun's vast sphere and through and beyond, to the other islands of the Sky, to the golden coasts of Sirius, in the Valley of Spirits of Arcturus —

O but it is indeed desirable, thus out of One goblet to drink with the belovèd the bliss of the world! Intoxicated with the blessèd cradle song that I sang to myself, I fell asleep in the midst of the glorious phantoms.

But when, in the beam of the morning light, the Earth once more caught fire, I looked up and sought the dreams of the night. They had disappeared like the beautiful Stars, and only the rapture of melancholy bore witness to them.

I mourned; but I believe that amongst the Blessèd one also mourns thus. She was the messenger of joy, this mourning, she was the coming dawn whereon bud the countless roses of the red morning Sky. —

The glowing Summer day had now frightened everything away into the dark shadows. Also around Diotima's house everything was still and empty and the jealous curtains stood in my way at all windows.

I lived in thoughts of her. Where are you, I thought, where can my lonely spirit find you, sweet maiden? Do you gaze before you and reflect? Have you put your work aside and rest your arm on your knee and your head on your little hand and give yourself up to dear thoughts?

May nothing disturb my peaceful one, when she refreshes her heart with sweet phantasies, O that nothing may touch this cluster of grapes and stroke the strengthening dew from the tender berries!

Thus I dreamt. But whilst my thoughts looked for her within the walls of the house, my feet sought her elsewhere, and before I was aware of it, I was walking under the arcades of the holy wood behind Diotima's garden, where I had seen her for the first time. How was that? I had indeed in the meantime, walked amongst these trees so often, had become more intimate with them, more calm amongst them, now a power seized me as though I trod in the shadow of Diana, to die before the actual divinity.

Meanwhile I went on. With every step it became more wonderful in me. I would have liked to fly, my heart so drove me forwards; but it was as though I had lead on my soles. The soul had gone on ahead and left the earthly limbs behind. I heard no more and before my eyes all forms dimmed and wavered. My spirit was already with Diotima; in the morning light played the tree-top whilst the lower branches still felt the cold dawn.

Ah! my Hyperion! a voice then called to me; I rushed towards it; "my Diotima! O my Diotima!" further had I no word and no breath, no consciousness.

Vanish, vanish, mortal life, poor commerce, where the lonely spirit examines and counts the pennies over and again, that he has collected! we all are called to the joy of the Divinity!

Here there is a gap in my existence. I died, and as I awoke I lay on the heart of the heavenly maiden.

O Life of Love! how you rose in her in full lovely bloom! as though sung into a light sleep by blessèd Genii, the charming little head lay on my shoulder, smiled sweet peace, and opened its ethereal eyes upon me in joyful inexperienced astonishment as though they looked for the first time into the world.

Long we stood thus in lovely unselfconscious contemplation, and neither knew what was happening to them, until finally joy increased too much in me and in tears and sounds of ecstasy my lost speech also began again, and completely woke my quiet enthusiast into life.

Finally, also, we looked about us again.

O my old friendly trees! cried Diotima, as though she had not seen them for a long time, and the remembrance of her former solitary days played sweetly about her joy, like the shadows round the virginal snow, when it reddens and glows in the joyful evening splendour.

Angel of Heaven! I cried, who can comprehend you? who can say he has fully understood you?

Do you wonder, she responded, that I so love you? Dear one! proud modest one! Am I then also one of those who cannot believe in you, have I then not fathomed you, have I not recognised the Genius in his clouds? Just disguise yourself and do not see yourself; I will conjure you out, I will —

But yes, he is there, he has risen, like a star; he has broken through the husk and stands, like a Springtime, there; like a crystal Spring out of the dark grotto, he has arisen; that is not the gloomy

Hyperion, that is the wild mourning no more — O my, my glorious youth!

That was all to me like a dream. Could I believe in this miracle of love? could I? the joy would have killed me.

Divine one! I cried, do you speak with me? can you deny yourself so, blessèd self-sufficient one! can you so delight in me? O I see it now, I know now what I often sensed, man is a garment, that a God often throws round himself, a chalice in which Heaven pours its nectar, to give his children the best to taste. —

Yes, yes! she broke in, smiling enthusiastically, your namesake, the glorious Hyperion of the Heavens, is in you.

Let me, I cried, let me be yours, let me forget myself, let all life in me and all spirit fly only to you; only you, in blessèd endless contemplation! O Diotima! thus I also stood formerly before the dawning image of a god, that my love created for itself, before the idol of my lonely dreams; I cherished it intimately; with my life I animated it, with the hopes of my heart I refreshed, warmed it, but it gave me nothing other than that which I had given, and when I became poor, it left me poor, and now! now I have you in my arms, and feel the breath of your breast, and feel your eye in my eye, the beautiful present flows into all my senses, and I endure it, thus I have the most glorious and tremble no more — yes! I am truly not what I once was, Diotima! I have become such as you, and Divine now plays with Divine, as children play amongst themselves. —

But for me you must be somewhat calmer, she said.

You are also right, you kind one! I cried joyfully, otherwise the Graces appear not to me; otherwise, indeed, I see not their soft beautiful movements in the sea of beauty. O I will yet learn it, to overlook nothing about you. Only give me time!

Flatterer! she cried, but for today we are finished, dear flatterer! the golden evening cloud has warned me. O mourn not! Preserve for you and me your pure joy! Let it echo in you until tomorrow, and do not kill it through discontent! — the flowers of the heart want friendly care. Their root is everywhere, but they themselves flourish only in serene weather. Fare well, Hyperion!

She disengaged herself. My whole being flamed up in me as she thus vanished from me in her glowing beauty.

O you! — I cried and rushed after her, and gave my soul into her hand in endless kisses.

God! she cried, to what will this lead!

That struck me. Forgive, divine one! I said; I go. Good night, Diotima, think of me a little!

That I will, she cried, good night!

And now no word more, Bellarmin! It would be too much for my patient heart. I am deeply affected by how I feel. But I will go out amongst the plants and the trees and lie down amongst them and pray that Nature may bring me to such peace.

HYPERION TO BELLARMIN

Our souls lived now ever more freely and beautifully together, and all within and around us united in golden peace. It seemed as though the old world had died and a new began with us, so spiritual and strong and loving and light had everything become, and we and all beings moved, spiritually united, like a chorus of a thousand indivisible tones, through the everlasting Aether.

Our conversations glided away like heavenly blue waters, through which the golden sand now and then gleamed, and our peace was, like the peace of the mountain peak, where in the glorious solitary height, high above the region of thunder, only the divine air still stirs in the locks of the bold wanderer.

And the wonderful holy mourning, when the hour of our parting sounded in our rapture, when I often cried: now we are again mortal, Diotima! and she said to me: mortality is illusion, like the colours, which waver before our eye when it has looked long into the Sun!

Ah! and all the lovely games of love! the flattering words, the anxieties, the sensibilities, the severity and forbearance.

And the omniscience, with which we saw through each other, and the unending faith with which we glorified each other!

Yes! a Sun is man, all seeing, transfigured, when he loves, and if he does not love, then is he a dark dwelling, wherein burns a little smoking lamp.

I should be silent, should forget and be silent.

But the enticing flame tempts me, until I completely throw myself into it, and like the fly, perish.

In the midst of all the blessèd irrepressible giving and taking I felt once that Diotima was becoming quieter and ever quieter.

I asked and pleaded; but that seemed to distance her still more, finally she implored me, not to ask any more, to go, and when I returned, to speak of something else. That then put me into a painful silence, in which I could not find my way.

It was to me as though an inexplicable sudden fate had sworn our love to death, and all life was gone, from me and everything.

Truly I was ashamed of this; I knew for certain, that chance did not rule Diotima's heart. But always she remained strange to me and my spoilt inconsolable mind always wanted declared actual love; reserved treasures were for me lost treasures. Ah! in fortune I had forgotten what I had learnt of hope, I was still then, like the impatient children, who weep for the apple on the tree, as though it were not there at all, because it is not kissing their mouth. I had no rest, I implored again, with impetuosity and humility, tenderly and angrily; with her complete all-powerful modest eloquence Love armoured me and then — O my Diotima! then I had it, the delightful confession, now I have it and hold it, until the surge of love brings also me, with all that is in me, back into the ancient home, into the bosom of Nature.

The innocent one! still she did not know the powerful abundance of her heart, and dearly shocked at the wealth in her, she buried it in the depth of her breast — and how she then confessed, divine simplicity, how with tears she confessed, she loved too much, and how she took leave of all that she once cradled in her heart, O how she cried: unfaithful I have been to May and Summer and Autumn, and pay no attention to the days and the night, as before, belong no longer to the Heavens and the Earth, belong to only One, One, but the blossom of May and the flame of Summer and the ripeness of the Autumn, the clarity of the day and the gravity of the night, and Earth and Heaven is united in this One! thus I love! — and how she then, in full heart's joy, looked at me, how she, in daring holy happiness, took me in her lovely arms and kissed my brow and mouth, ha! how the divine head, dying in wonder, sank down onto my bare neck, and the sweet lips rested on my beating breast and the dear breath went into my soul — O Bellarmin! my senses fade away and my spirit flees.

I see, I see how it must end. The rudder has fallen into the waves and, like a child by the feet, the ship will be seized and cast onto the rocks.

HYPERION TO BELLARMIN

There are great periods in life. We look up to them as to the colossal figures of the future and antiquity, we fight a glorious fight with them, and if we stand our ground, they become, as sisters, and leave us not.

We sat once together on our mountain, on a stone of the ancient city of this island and spoke of how, here the lion Demosthenes had found his end, how he here with holy self-appointed death had achieved freedom from the Macedonian chains and daggers — The glorious spirit went jestingly out of the world, cried one; why not? I said; he had nothing more here to seek; Athens had become Alexander's whore, and the world like a stag hunted to death by the great hunter.

O Athens! cried Diotima; I have sometimes mourned when I looked out there, and out of the blue dusk the phantom of Olympieum rose up before me!

How far is it across? I asked.

A day's journey perhaps, replied Diotima.

A day's journey, I cried, and I had not yet been over there? We must immediately go over together.

Absolutely! cried Diotima; tomorrow we have calm sea, and

everything stands now still in its green and ripeness.

One needs the eternal Sun and the life of the immortal Earth for such a pilgrimage.

Tomorrow then! I said, and our friends agreed.

We travelled early, to the song of the cockerel from the roadside. We and the world shone in fresh clarity. Golden peaceful youth was in our hearts. The life in us was, like the life of a newborn island of the ocean, on which the first Spring begins.

For a long time more equilibrium had come into my soul under Diotima's influence; today I felt it three times as purely, and the scattered enthusing powers were all gathered into One golden mean.

We spoke with one another of the excellence of the Athenian people, from whence they came, of what they consisted.

One said, the climate had made them; the other: art and philosophy; the third: religion and form of government.

Athenian art and religion, and philosophy and form of government, I said, are the blossom and fruits of the tree, not ground and root. You are taking the effect for the cause.

But he who says to me, that the climate has created all this, let him reflect that we also still live in it.

More undisturbed in every respect, of powerful influence freer than any people on Earth, the Athenian people grew up. No conqueror weakens them, no fortune of war intoxicates them, no foreign polytheism deadens them, no rash wisdom drives them to untimely fruition. Left to itself, like the growing diamond, is its childhood. One hears practically nothing of them until the times of Pisistratus and Hipparchus. Only a small part did they take in the Trojan War that, as in the hot house, heated and animated the majority of the Greek peoples too early. — No unusual fate produces the people. Great and colossal are the sons of such a mother, but beautiful beings, or, what is the same, men, they will never become, or only late, then when the oppositions have battled with each other too severely not to finally make peace.

In exuberant strength Lacedaemon hastens ahead of the Athenians and for that reason would have become loose and dissipated earlier had Lycurgus not come, and with discipline restrained the high-spirited nature. From then on was also, everything with the Spartans cultivated, all excellence won and purchased through diligence and self-conscious effort, and as far as one can in a certain sense speak of the simplicity of the Spartans, they however did not naturally have complete, real childlike simplicity. The Lacedaemonians broke through the order of instinct too early, they degenerated too early and therefore discipline had to begin with them too early; for every discipline and art begins too early where the nature of man has not yet matured. Perfect nature must live in the human child, before it goes into school, so that the image of childhood may show him the return from school back to perfect Nature.

The Spartans remain always a fragment; for he who was not a complete child will hardly become a complete man. —

Certainly Heaven and Earth also played their part for the Athenians, as for all Greeks, did not offer them poverty or excess. The beams of Heaven did not fall on them like a rain of fire. The Earth did not coddle and intoxicate them with caresses and extravagant gifts, as here and there the foolish mother otherwise does.

In addition to this came the wonderful great deed of Theseus, the voluntary restriction of his own royal power.

O! such a grain of seed thrown into the heart of the people must give rise to an ocean of golden ears of corn, and evidently works and continues to grow abundantly still late amongst the Athenians.

Thus, once more! the fact that the Athenians grew up so free of powerful influences of any sort, on such moderate sustenance, that made them so excellent, and that alone could achieve it!

Leave man undisturbed in the cradle! do not drive him out of the closely fused bud of his being, do not drive him out of the little cot of his childhood! Do not do so little that he cannot do without you and thus distinguish you from himself, do not do too much, so that he does not feel your or his power and thus distinguish you from himself, in short do not let man know until later, that there are men, that there is something beyond himself, for only then will he become man. For man is a God as soon as he is man. And if he is a God, then he is beautiful.

Strange! cried one of the friends.

You have never spoken so deeply out of my soul, cried Diotima.

I have it from you, I rejoined.

Thus was the Athenian a man, I continued, thus he had to become. Beautiful, he came out of the hands of Nature, beautiful in body and soul as it is said.

The first child of human, of divine Beauty, is art. In her, divine man rejuvenates and repeats himself. He wants to be aware of himself, therefore he confronts himself with his beauty. Thus man gave himself his Gods. For in the beginning man and his Gods were one, when, unknown to itself, there was divine beauty. — I speak of mysteries, but they exist. —

The first child of divine beauty is art. Thus it was with the Athenians.

Beauty's second daughter is religion. Religion is love of Beauty. The wise man loves it itself, the infinite, the all-embracing; the people love her children, the Gods, who in manifold forms appear to them. It was also thus with the Athenians. And without such love of beauty, without such religion, every state is a dry skeleton without life or spirit, and all thought and action a tree without a crown, a column from which the capital has been struck down.

But that this was really the case with the Greeks and particularly the Athenians, that their art and their religion are the genuine children of eternal Beauty — perfected human nature — and could only have arisen from perfected human nature, that is clearly shown if one will just look at the subjects of their holy art and religion with an unprejudiced eye, how they loved and honoured each object.

Faults and false steps occur everywhere and also here. But it is certain that one mostly finds mature man in the objects of his art. There is not the trivial, not the monstrous of the Egyptians and Goths, there is human intelligence and human form. They veer less than the others to the extremes of the metaphysical and the physical. In the beautiful mean of humanity, their Gods remain, more than the others.

And like the object, so also love. Not too slavish and not too familiar! —

From the beauty of the spirit of the Athenian there followed then the necessary disposition for freedom.

The Egyptian bears without pain the despotism of arbitrary

action, the son of the North, without aversion, the law of despotism, injustice in the form of justice; for the Egyptian has from the womb an instinct for homage and idolatry; in the North one believes too little in the pure free life of Nature, not to superstitiously depend upon the law.

The Athenian cannot tolerate despotism, because his divine nature does not want to be disturbed, he cannot tolerate legality everywhere, because he does not need it everywhere. Draco is no good for him. He wants to be handled gently, and is right in this.

Good! someone interrupted me, that I understand, but, how this poetic religious people should also be a philosophical people, that I do not see.

They would, said I, not even have become a philosophical people without poetry!

What has philosophy, he retorted, what has the cold eminence of this science to do with poetry?

Poetry, I said, sure of this, is the beginning and the end of this science. Like Minerva from the head of Jupiter, she arose out of the poetry of an infinite divine Being. And so finally, the incompatible will once again flow into it, into the mysterious source of poetry.

That is a paradoxical man, cried Diotima, however, I sense his meaning. But you digress. We were talking of Athens.

The man, I began again, who at least once in life does not feel within himself complete pure beauty, when the powers of his being, like the colours of the rainbow, play amongst one another, who never experienced as only in periods of enthusiasm, how everything all comes intimately together, that man will never become a philosophical sceptic, his spirit is not even capable of demolishing, let alone constructing. For believe me, the reason the sceptic finds in everything, that is thought, only contradictions and flaws, is because he knows the harmony of flawless beauty, that can never be thought. The dry bread, that human reason well meaningly offers him, he scorns, only because he is secretly feasting at the Table of the Gods.

Enthusiast! cried Diotima, for that reason you also became a sceptic. But the Athenians!

I am just about to come to them, I said. The great saying ἐν διαφερον ἑαυτῳ (the One differentiated in itself)) of Heraclitus, could only have been lit upon by a Greek, for it is the essence of Beauty, and before that had been discovered, there was no philosophy.

Now it could be determined, the whole existed. The flower had blossomed; one could now dissect.

The moment of Beauty had become manifest amongst men, was there in life and soul, the Infinitely United existed.

One could analyse it, resolve it in spirit, could rethink the separated anew, could thus more and more understand the nature of the highest and best and translate the understood into precepts in the manifold areas of the spirit.

Do you see now, why the Athenians in particular also had to be a philosophical people?

The Egyptian could not. He who does not live in equal love with and from Heaven and Earth, who does not in this sense live with the elements in which he moves, is naturally also not so unified within himself, and does not so easily experience eternal Beauty like a Greek.

Like a magnificent despot, the oriental zone throws its inhabitants to the ground with its power and splendour, and, before man has even learnt to walk, he has to kneel, before he has learnt to speak, he has to pray; before his heart has found a balance, he has to bow it, and before the spirit is strong enough to bear flowers and fruit, Fate and Nature draws all strength out of it with burning heat. The Egyptian is sacrificed, before he is a whole, and therefore he knows nothing of wholeness, nothing of beauty, and that which he names the highest is a veiled power, a terrifying enigma; the mute dark Isis is his First and Last, an empty infinity and from that nothing reasonable has ever come. Even from the most sublime Nothing, nothing will be born.

The North, on the contrary, drives its pupils too early into themselves, and if the spirit of the fiery Egyptians hurries out into the world with too much desire to travel, in the North the spirit prepares to return back into itself, before it is even ready to travel.

In the North one has to be intelligent, even before there is a mature feeling in one, one lays the blame on oneself for everything, even before naïveté has reached its beautiful end; one has to be rational, has to become a self-conscious intellect, before one is a man, a wise man before one is a child; the unity of the whole man, beauty, is not allowed to grow and mature in him, before he forms and develops his mind. Pure intellect, pure reason are always kings in the North.

But from pure intellect there has come nothing intelligent, from pure reason nothing reasonable.

Intellect is without spiritual beauty, like a subservient journeyman who makes a fence out of rough wood, from a plan that is sketched out for him, and nails the cut posts together for the garden that the master will design and plant. The whole business of the intellect is work of necessity. From folly and from wrong it protects us, whilst it regulates; but to be safe from folly and wrong is certainly not the highest level of human excellence.

Reason is without beauty of spirit and heart, like a slave-driver, whom the master of the house has set above the servants; he knows as little as the servants what is to come out of all the endless work, and just shouts: bestir yourselves, and almost does not like to see, when it goes too quickly, for at the end he will have nothing more to drive, and his rôle would have been played.

Out of mere intellect could come no philosophy, for philosophy is more than the limited perception of what is present.

Out of mere reason could come no philosophy, for philosophy is more than the blind demand of a never-ending progress of reconciliation and differentiation of a possible material.

But if the divine ἐν διαφερον ἑαυτῳ, the ideal of beauty, illumines the striving reason, then it does not demand blindly, and knows why that purpose it demands.

If, like the May day into the artist's studio, the Sun of Beauty shines into reason as it works, then it does not rush out, it is true, and leave its necessary work standing, but thinks gladly of the holiday, where it will wander in the rejuvenating Spring light.

I was so far when we landed on the coast of Attica.

Ancient Athens was too much in our minds, for us to want to classify it in speech, and I now myself wondered at the nature of my assertions. How, I cried, did I come upon the barren mountain peak on which you saw me?

It is always so, responded Diotima, when one is very happy. The abundant energy seeks something to do. The young lambs knock their foreheads together when they are replete with their mother's milk.

We were now walking up Mount Lycabettus, and despite the hurry, occasionally stood in thought and wonderful anticipation.

It is good that it is so difficult for man to convince himself of the death of that which he loves, and there is probably still no one who has gone to his friend's grave, without the slight hope of actually meeting his friend there. I was seized by the beautiful phantom of Ancient Athens, like a mother figure who returns from the realm of the dead.

O Parthenon! I cried, pride of the world! to your feet lies the realm of Neptune like a vanquished lion, and like children, the other temples are gathered round you, and the eloquent Agora and the Grove of Academia —

Can you so transport yourself into ancient times, said Diotima.

Do not remind me of the time! I retorted; it was a divine life and man was there the centre of nature. He was the Spring as it blossomed around Athens like a shy flower on a maiden's breast; the Sun rose up blushingly over the glory of the Earth.

The marble cliffs of Hymettus and Pentele sprang forth from their lulling cradles, like children from their mother's lap, and won form and life under the tender Athenian hands.

Honey, Nature offered, and the most beautiful violets and myrtles and olives.

Nature was priestess and man her god, and all life in her and each form and each tone from her just One rapturous echo of the glorious one, to whom she belonged.

Celebrated him, to him only she sacrificed.

He was also worthy of it, he liked to lovingly sit in the divine workshop and embrace the knees of the image of the god, that he had made, or on the promontory on Sunium's green headland, couched amongst the hearkening students, while away the time with great thoughts, or he liked to run in the stadium, or from the orator's chair, like the Thunder God, send rain and sunshine and lightning and golden Clouds —

O look! cried Diotima suddenly to me.

I looked, and could have died at the overpowering sight.

Like an immense shipwreck, when the hurricanes have become silent and the sailors have escaped, and the corpse of the shattered fleet lies, unrecognisable, on the sandbank, so Athens lay before us, and the deserted columns stood before us, like the bare trunks of a forest, which in the evening, is still green, and upon the night is consumed by fire.

Here, said Diotima, one learns to be quiet about one's own fate, be it good or bad.

Here one learns to be quiet about everything, I continued. Had the reapers, who mowed this cornfield, enriched their barns with the stalks, then nothing would have been lost, and I would have contented myself, to stand here as gleaner; but who then would gain?

The whole of Europe, retorted one of the friends.

O, yes, I cried, they have carted away the columns and statues and sold them to one another, have mainly valued their noble forms, for their curiosity, as one values parrots and apes.

Do not say that! rejoined the same; and if they lacked the spirit of all the beauty, it would be, because it could not be carried away and not sold.

Just so! I cried. This spirit perished well before the destroyers came upon Attica. Only when the houses and temples have died out, do the wild animals venture through the gates and the streets.

For he who has that spirit, said Diotima comfortingly, Athens still stands, like a blossoming fruit tree. The artist easily restores the torso for himself.

The next day we went out early, and saw the ruins of the Parthenon, the site of the ancient Theatre of Bacchus, the Temple of Theseus, the sixteen columns, that remain still standing, of the divine Olympieum; but above all I was moved by the ancient gate, through which one formerly came out of the old city into the new, where, certainly once, a thousand beautiful people on one day would have greeted one another. Now one could come into neither the old or the new city through this gate, and silent and deserted, it stands there, like a dried-up fountain, from whose conduits there once with pleasant plashing, gushed clear fresh water.

Ah! I said, whilst we thus walked around, it is probably an excellent sport of Fate, that she here overthrows the temples and gives their shattered stones to the children to toss about, that she gives the mutilated Gods as benches for the front of peasant huts, and the gravestones here makes into a resting place for the grazing bulls; and such an extravagance is more regal, than the wantonness of Cleopatra, when she drank the melted pearls; but yet it is a pity about all the Greatness and Beauty!

Good Hyperion! cried Diotima, it is time that you went; you are pale and your eye is tired, and you seek in vain for fancies to help you. Come out! into the verdure! amongst the colours of life! that will do you good.

We went out into the nearby gardens.

The others had, on the way, got into conversation with two British scholars, who were celebrating their harvest amongst the antiquities in Athens, and were not to be moved. I left them gladly.

My whole being arose, when I saw myself once more alone with Diotima; she had undergone a glorious battle with the divine chaos of Athens. Like the stringed music of the heavenly Muse over the variant elements, Diotima's quiet thoughts prevailed over the ruins. Like the moon out of a delicate cloud mass, her spirit rose up out of beautiful sorrow; the heavenly maiden stood there in her melancholy, like a flower which prefers to give out its perfume in the night.

We went further and further, and finally, had not walked in vain.

O you Groves of Angele, where the olive tree and the cypress, whispering round each other, cool themselves with friendly shades, where the golden fruit of the lemon tree shines from the dark foliage, where the swelling grape wantonly grows over the fence, and the ripe orange, like a smiling foundling, lies in the way! you fragrant homely paths! you peaceful seats where the image of the myrtle bush smiles out of the Spring! I will never forget you.

Diotima and I walked about for a while under the glorious trees, until a large clearing offered itself to us.

Here we sat down. There was a blessed stillness between us. My spirit hovered around the divine form of the maiden, like the butterfly a flower, and all my being lightened, became united in the joy of enraptured contemplation.

Are you once again consoled, light-minded one?

Yes, yes! I am, I replied. That which I supposed lost, I have; that which I pined for as though it had disappeared from the world, that is before me. No, Diotima! the source of Eternal Beauty has still not dried up.

I have already said it to you once, I need Gods and man no more. I know Heaven is deserted, depopulated, and the Earth, that once overflowed with beautiful human life, has become almost like an ant heap. But there is still a place, where the old Heaven and the old Earth laughs at me. For all the Gods of heaven and all divine men of earth I forget in you.

What do I care for the shipwreck of the world, I know of nought, but my Blessèd Isle.

There is a time of Love, said Diotima with friendly earnestness, as there is a time to live in the happy cradle. But life itself drives us out.

Hyperion! — here she grasped my hand with fervour, and her voice rose with power — it seems to me that you are born to higher things. Do not misjudge yourself! the lack of material held you back. It did not go fast enough. That cast you down. Like the young gladiators you attacked too quickly, even before your goal was certain and your hand skilled, and because you, as is natural, were more struck, than you struck yourself, you became shy and doubted yourself and everything; for you are as sensitive as you are passionate. But nothing is lost thereby. Had your disposition and your efficacy matured so early, your spirit would not be what it is; you would not have been the thinking man if you had not been the suffering man, of turbulent soul. Believe me, you would never have known the equilibrium of beautiful humanity so purely if you had not lost it so much. Your heart has finally found peace. I want to believe it. I understand it. But do you really think that you now are at the end? Will you lock yourself in the heaven of your love, and leave the world that needs you, parched and cold, beneath you? You must, like the ray of light, descend like the all-refreshing rain, you must go down into the land of mortals, you must enlighten like Apollo, shake, enliven like Jupiter, otherwise you are not worthy of your heaven. I ask you, go once more into Athens, and also observe the people that go around amongst the ruins, the rough Albanians and the other good childish Greeks, who, with a jolly dance and a holy fairy tale, console themselves for the abusive power that oppresses them — can you say, I am ashamed of this material? I think, on the contrary, it would still be cultivable. Can you turn your heart away from the needy? They are not bad, they have done nothing to hurt you!

What can I do for them, I cried.

Give them what you have within you, replied Diotima, give —

No word, no word more, great soul! I cried, otherwise you bend me, otherwise it is as though you had brought me to it by force —

They will not be happier, but nobler, no! they will also be happier. They must arise, they must come forth, like the young mountains from the waves of the sea, when a subterranean fire drives them.

It is true I stand alone and walk without fame amongst them. Yet one, who is a man, can he not do more, than hundreds who are only parts of men?

Divine Nature! you are the same within and without me. It must not be so difficult, to unite that which is without me with the Divinity within me. Indeed, the bee succeeds in its small realm, why then should not I not be able to plant and build, what is necessary?

What? the Arabian merchant broadcast his Koran, and there grew up for him a folk of pupils like an unending forest, and that soil should also not flourish, where the ancient truth returns in new living youth?

It will be fundamentally different! From the roots of mankind a new world shall spring! A new deity rule over them, a new future brighten before them.

In the workshop, in the houses, in the assemblies, in the temples, everywhere it will be different!

But I must still go forth to learn. I am an artist, but I am not skilled. I compose in spirit, but I do not know how to guide my hand —

You go to Italy, said Diotima, to Germany, France — how many years do you need? three — four — I think three are enough; you are not one of the slow ones, and seek only the Greatest and the most Beautiful —

"And then?"

You will be the educator of our people, you will be a great man, I hope. And when I thus then embrace you, then I will dream, as though I were part of the glorious man, then I will exult, as though you had given me the half of your immortality, like Pollux to Castor, O! I will be a proud maiden, Hyperion!

I was silent a while. I was full of inexpressible happiness.

Is there then contentment between the decision and the deed, I began again finally, is there repose before the victory?

It is the repose of a hero, said Diotima, there are decisions that, like the words of Gods, are at the same time command and fulfil-ment, and so it is with yours —

We went back as after the first embrace. Everything had become to us strange and new to us.

I stood now above the ruins of Athens, like the husbandman in the fallow field. Just lie peacefully, I thought, when we once more went to the ship, just lie peacefully, sleeping land! Soon young life will spring from you, and grow towards the blessings of Heaven. Soon, the Clouds will never in vain, send rain, soon the Sun will find its ancient pupils once more.

You would ask after man, Nature? You lament, like a lyre, on which only the wind, the brother of chance, plays, because the artist, who directs it, has died? They will come, your men, Nature! A rejuvenated people will rejuvenate you also, and you will be, as its bride, and the old community of spirits will be revived with you.

There will be only One beauty; and Humanity and Nature will unite in One all-embracing Divinity.

SECOND VOLUME

*μη φυναι τον άπαντα νικα λογον. το δ᾽ έπει φανη, βηναι κειθεν
όθεν περ ήκει, πολυ δευτερον, ώς ταχιστα.*

SOPHOCLES

FIRST BOOK

HYPERION TO BELLARMIN

We lived in the last lovely moments of the year, after our return from the Attic country.

A brother of Spring was the Autumn to us, full of mild fires, a festival for the memory of pain and past joys of love. The fading leaves bore the colour of the sunset glow, only the pine and the laurel stood in eternal green. The migrating birds lingered in the bright airs, others revelled in the vineyard and in the garden, and reaped joyfully, that which people had left. And the heavenly Light ran pure from a clear sky, through all the branches smiled the holy Sun, the kind one, whom I never name without joy and thanks, who oft in deep sorrow had healed me with one glance, and of ill-humour and cares purified my soul.

We visited again all our dearest paths, Diotima and I, vanished blessèd hours encountered us everywhere.

We reminded ourselves of the past May, we had never seen the Earth as then, we said, it had been transformed, a silver cloud of blossom, a joyful flame of life, freed of all baser matter.

Ah! all was so full of joy and hope, cried Diotima, so full of unceasing growth and yet also so effortless, so blessedly calm like a child that plays by itself and thinks no further.

Thereby, I cried, I recognise her, the Soul of Nature, by this secret fire, by this lingering in her mighty haste.

And it is so dear to the happy, this lingering, cried Diotima; do you know, once of an evening we stood together on the bridge, after a great storm, and the red mountain waters shot away beneath us like an arrow, but nearby, the woods grew in peace, and the bright beech leaves hardly stirred. It did us so much good, that the soulful green did not also flee away from us, like the stream, and the beautiful Spring stayed so peacefully for us, like a tame bird, but now however it is beyond the mountains.

We smiled at the words, although mourning was closer to us.

So also shall our own blessedness depart, and we foresaw it.

O Bellarmin! who may then say he stands fast, when even the Beautiful thus ripens towards its fate, when also the Divine must humble itself, and share mortality with all that is mortal!

HYPERION TO BELLARMIN

I had lingered still with the lovely maiden before her house, until the light of night shone in the peaceful gloaming, then I returned to Notara's dwelling, thoughtful, full of overflowing heroic life, as always, when I came from her embraces. A letter from Alabanda had come.

Things are stirring, Hyperion, he wrote to me, Russia has declared war on The Sublime Porte; they are coming with a fleet into the Archipelago*; the Greeks shall be free when they rise up together, to drive the Sultan to the Euphrates. The Greeks will do their part, the Greeks will be free and I am heartily pleased, that there is once more something to do. I did not like to see the day, as long as no progress was made.

If you are still your old self, then come! You'll find me in the village before Coron, if you come by way of Mistra. I live by the hill in the white cottage at the edge of the woods.

The men that you met with me in Smyrna, I have left. You were right with your finer sense, not to enter their circle.

I long to see us both again in the new life. For you, the world up to now was too bad for you to make yourself known to it. Because you did not want to do menial work, you did nothing, and inaction made you morose and dreamy.

You did not want to swim in the swamp. Come now, come, and let us bathe in the open Sea!

It will do us good, my only belovèd!

Thus he wrote. I was confounded in the first moment. My face burnt with shame, my heart boiled like, hot springs, and I could not remain still, it so pained me to be thus surpassed by Alabanda, subdued forever. But now I took the future task to heart all the more eagerly. —

I have been too idle, I cried, too peace loving, too ethereal, too inactive! — Alabanda looks into the world, like a noble pilot, Alabanda is industrious and seeks spoils in the eddy; and your hands sleep in your lap? and you want to make do with words, and conjure the world with magic formulæ? But your words, like snowflakes, are useless and only make the air gloomier, and your incantations are for the devout, but the unbelievers hear you not. — Yes! to be gentle at the right time, that is indeed good, but to be gentle at the wrong time, that is odious, for it is cowardly! — But Harmodius! your myrtle I will resemble, your myrtle wherein the sword hid itself. I do not want to have gone idle in vain, and my sleep shall become like oil when the flame is introduced. I do not want to look on, when the moment comes, do not want to go around and inquire of the news, when Alabanda takes the laurel.

* In the Year 1770

HYPERION TO BELLARMIN

Diotima's pallor, as she read Alabanda's letter, pierced my soul. She then began, calmly and seriously, to advise me against taking such a step and, in continual exchange, we said much. O you violent ones! she cried finally, you who are so quick to go to extremes, think of Nemesis!

He who can suffer the extreme, said I, for him the extreme is right.

Even if it is right, she said, you are not born to it.

So it would appear, I said; I have also delayed long enough. O I would like to load an Atlas upon me, to pay the debts of my youth. Have I a consciousness? have I an abiding place in me? O allow me, Diotima! Here, in just such a task, I must capture it.

That is vain presumption! cried Diotima; quite recently you were more modest, recently when you said, I must still go forth, to learn.

Dear Sophist! I cried, then the subject in question was something completely different. To the Olympus of Divine Beauty, where out of eternally youthful Springs the Truth with all Goodness arises, thither to lead my people, I am still not yet capable. But to use a sword, I have learnt, and for now no more is necessary. The new Covenant of Spirits cannot live in the air, the holy Theocracy of the Beautiful must live in a free state, and it wants to have a place on Earth and this place we will certainly conquer.

You will conquer, cried Diotima, and forget for what? will, at most, enforce a free state for yourself and then say, wherefore have I built? ah! it will be consumed, all the beautiful life that in that very place should make itself felt, will be spent, even in you! The fierce battle will tear you to pieces, beautiful soul, you will age, blessèd spirit! and, world-weary, finally ask, where are you now, you ideals of my youth?

That is cruel, Diotima, I cried, to so touch my heart, to so hold me fast, by my own fear of death, by my highest love of life, but no! no! no! menial work kills, but righteous war brings each soul alive. That gives gold the colour of the Sun, that one casts it into the fire! That, that first gives man his whole youth, that he breaks chains. That alone saves him, that he rises up and crushes the viper, the creeping century that poisons all Nature at source! — Age, shall I Diotima! if I free Greece? age, become poor, a common man? O so then he was probably most shallow and empty and god-forsaken, the Athenian youth, when, as the messenger of victory from Marathon, he came over the summit of Pentelicus and looked down into the valleys of Attica!

Dear One! Dear One! cried Diotima, just be calm! I will not say another word to you. You shall go, shall go, proud man! Ah! when you are thus, I have no power, no right over you.

She cried bitterly and I stood like a criminal before her. Forgive me, divine girl! I cried, sunk down before her, O forgive me, whither I must! I choose not, I reflect not. A force is in me and I do not know, whether it is myself that drives me to this step. Your whole Soul commands you, she answered. Not to follow her, often leads to downfall, yet, to follow her, probably also. The best is, you go, for it is greater. You act; I will bear it.

HYPERION TO BELLARMIN

Diotima was from now on wonderfully changed.

With joy I had seen how, since our love, the reticent life had opened out in looks and loving words and her genius-inspired calm had often met me in shining enthusiasm.

But how so strange the beautiful Soul becomes to us, when, after the first blooming, after the morning of her course, she has to rise up to the heights of noon. One hardly knew the blessèd child anymore, so noble and so passive had she become.

O how often I lay before the sorrowing divine image, and fancied I had wept away my soul in agony for her, and stood up marvelling and full myself of all-powerful strengths! A flame had advanced into her eye from her oppressed breast. It had become too confined for her in the bosom full of longing and suffering; therefore were the thoughts of the maiden so glorious and bold. A new power, a visible authority over all that could feel, ruled in her. She was a higher being. She belonged to mortal men no more.

O my Diotima, if I had then thought to what it would come?

HYPERION TO BELLARMIN

Also the wise Notara became enchanted by the new plans, promised me a strong faction, hoped soon to occupy the Corinthian Isthmus and, like a handle, there to seize Greece. But Fate would have it otherwise and rendered his labour useless, before it achieved its goal.

He advised me, not to go to Tenos, to travel directly down, and out through the Peloponnese, as inconspicuously as possible. My father I should write to on the way, he thought, the cautious old man would more easily forgive a step already taken, than allow one that had not taken place. To my mind that was not right, but we so gladly sacrifice our own feelings, when a great goal stands before us.

I doubt, continued Notara, whether, in such a case, you will be able to reckon on your father's help. Therefore I give you, what is incidentally necessary for you, at all events, to live and work for a while. If one day you can, then you pay me back, if not, then mine was also yours. Do not be ashamed of money, he added, smiling; even the steeds of Phoebus do not live on air alone, as the poets tell us.

HYPERION TO BELLARMIN

Then came the day of parting.

For the morning I had remained up in Notara's garden in the fresh Winter air, amongst the evergreen cypresses and cedars. I was composed. The great strength of youth uplifted me and the suffering, of which I had a presentiment, carried me like a cloud, higher.

Diotima's mother had asked Notara and the other friends and me if we would like to spend the last day together with her. Diotima and I had gladdened the kindly ones and the divinity in our love had not gone unnoticed by them. They should now also bless my departure.

I went down. I found the dear maiden at the hearth. It seemed to her a holy sacerdotal occupation, on this day to look after the house. She had made everything tidy, decorated everything in the house, and no one was allowed to help her. All the flowers, that were still left in the garden, she had gathered, roses and fresh grapes in the late season she had also collected.

She knew my footstep as I came up, came softly towards me; her pale cheeks glowed from the flame of the hearth and the serious widened eyes glittered with tears. She saw how overcome I was. Go in, my dear, she said; mother is inside and I will follow immediately.

I went in. There sat the noble woman and held out her beautiful hand to me — come, she cried, come, my son! I should be angry with you, you have taken my child from me, have dissuaded me from reason, and do what you desired and go hence; but forgive him for it, you heavenly powers! if he purposes wrong; and if he is right, O then delay not with your help for the dear one! I wanted to speak, but just then Notara came in with the other friends and behind them Diotima.

We were silent for a while. We honoured the sorrowing Love that was in us all; in her presence we were frightened of being overweening in speech and proud thoughts. Finally, after a few fleeting words, Diotima asked me to relate something of Agis and Cleomenes; I had often mentioned the great souls by name with fiery esteem and said they were Demigods, as much as Prometheus, and their fight with the fate of Sparta was more heroic than any other in the splendid myths. The genius of these men was the Sunset of the Greek day, as Theseus's and Homer's were the Aurora.

I related the story and at the end we all felt ourselves stronger and more sublime.

Fortunate, cried one of the friends, whose life alternates between heart's joy and lively combat.

Yes, cried another, that is Eternal Youth, that there are always enough forces in play and we fully maintain ourselves in work and pleasure.

O I would like to come with you, cried Diotima to me.

It is also good that that you stay, Diotima! I said. The priestess may not leave the temple. You keep the Holy Flame, you keep in peace the Beautiful, so that I find it again in you.

You are also right, my dear, that is better, she said, and her voice wavered and her ethereal eyes hid themselves in a handkerchief, not to allow their tears, their embarrassment, to be seen.

O Bellarmin! my heart wanted to break, that I had made her so blush with shame. Friends! I cried, keep this angel for me. I know of nothing more, if I do not know her. O Heaven! I dare not think, of what I would be capable, if I lost her.

Be calm, Hyperion! Notara broke in.

Calm? I cried; O you good people! you can often care how the garden grows, or how the harvest will be, you can pray for your vine, and I should part without wishes from the only one, whom my soul serves?

No, O you good one! cried Notara, moved, no! for me you shall not part from her without wishes! no, by the heavenly innocence of your love! you have my blessing certainly.

You remind me, I cried quickly. She shall bless us, this dear mother, shall with you, bear witness for us — come Diotima! our union shall be sanctified by your mother, until the beautiful community that we hope for, shall marry us.

Thus I fell on one knee; wide-eyed, blushing, solemnly smiling, she also sank down by my side.

For a long time, I cried, O Nature! our life has been one with yours and divinely youthful, like you and all your Gods, is our own world, through Love.

In your groves we wandered, continued Diotima, and were as you, by your Springs we sat and were as you, there over the mountains we went, with your children, the stars, as you.

When we were away from one another, I cried, when, like the whispering of a harp our coming delight first sounded to us, when we found each other, when there was no more sleep and all tones in us awoke to life's complete chords, divine Nature! then we were always, as you, and also now that we part and joy dies, we are, as you, full of sorrow and yet kindly disposed, therefore shall a pure mouth bear witness, that our love is holy and eternal, as you.

I bear witness, pronounced the mother.

We bear witness, cried the others.

Now there was no word left for us to say. I felt in the best of hearts; I felt myself ready for the parting. Now I will go forth, you dear ones! I said, and the life fled from all faces. Diotima stood like a marble effigy and I felt her hand die in mine. I had killed everything around me, I was alone and I became faint before the endless silence, in which my overflowing life found a hold no more.

Ah! I cried, it is burning hot in my heart, and you stand all so cold, you dear ones! and only the household gods give favourable hearing? — Diotima! you are silent, you do not see ! — O it is well for you that you do not see!

Just go, she sighed, yes it has to be; just go, you dear heart!

O sweet tone from these blissful lips! I cried, and stood like a worshipper before the lovely statue — sweet tone! just Once more breathe on me, just Once more dawn, dear light of your eyes!

Do not speak so, dear! she cried, speak to me more seriously, speak to me with greater heart!

I wanted to stop myself, but I was as in a dream.

Woe! I cried, that is no departure, where one returns.

You will kill her, cried Notara. Look how delicate she is, and you are so beside yourself.

I looked at her and tears flowed, burning, from my eyes.

So then farewell, Diotima! I cried, Heaven of my love, farewell! — Let us be strong, dear friends! dear mother! I gave you joy and sorrow! Farewell! farewell!

I reeled out. Diotima followed me alone.

The evening had come and the stars rose in the Heavens. We stood still below the house. Eternity was in us, above us. Tenderly, like the Aether, Diotima embraced me. Foolish one, what then is parting? she whispered mysteriously to me, with the smile of an immortal.

It is also now with me different, I said, and I do not know which of them is dream, my sorrow or my joy.

Both are, she returned, and both are good.

Perfect one! I cried, I speak as you. In the starry heavens we will recognise each other. Let it be a sign between you and me, for as long as our lips cease to sound.

So be it! she pronounced with a slow, never-before-heard tone — it was her last. In the dusk her image vanished from me and I do not know, whether it was really she, whom I embraced for the final time and whose fading form flashed just for a moment before my eyes and then departed into the night.

HYPERION TO BELLARMIN

Why do I relate this to you and repeat my suffering and excite my restless youth again within me? Is it not enough, Once to have travelled through mortality? why do I not remain in the peace of my spirit, still?

For this reason, my Bellarmin! because every breath one draws of life remains dear to our heart, because every change of innocent Nature also belongs together to her beauty. Our Soul, if she puts aside the mortal experiences and lives solely in divine repose, is she not like a leafless tree? like a head without locks? Dear Bellarmin! I have rested awhile; like a child, I have lived amongst the peaceful hills of Salamis, forgetful of Fate and the striving of mankind. Since then my view has become somewhat different, and I have now enough peace in me, to be able to remain calm, with each glimpse into human life. O Friend! at the end the Spirit reconciles us with all. You will not believe it, at least not from me. But I think, you should see it even in my letters, how my Soul becomes daily quieter and quieter. And in future I will say so much about it, until you believe it.

Here are letters from Diotima and myself, that we wrote to each other after my departure from Calaurea. They are the dearest things that I entrust to you. They are the warmest picture from those days of my life. Of the tumult of war they tell you little. All the more of my own life and that indeed, is what you want. Ah and you must also see, how loved I was. That I could never tell you, that says only Diotima.

HYPERION TO DIOTIMA

I have awoken from the death of parting, my Diotima! strengthened, as after sleep, my Soul arises.

I am writing to you from a peak of the Epidaurian mountains. There, far in the depths, dawns your island, Diotima! and out there my stadium, where I must win or fall. O Peloponnese! O you sources of Eurotas and Alpheus! There will be the question. Out from the Spartan forests, there, like an eagle, the ancient Genius of the nation will plunge, with our armies, as with thundering pinions.

My Soul is full of desire for action and full of love, Diotima, and my eye looks out into the Greek valleys, as though it could magically command: rise again, you Cities of the Gods!

A God must be in me, because also I hardly feel our parting. Like the holy shades beside Lethe, my soul now lives with yours in heavenly freedom and Fate has dominion over our love no more.

HYPERION TO DIOTIMA

I am now in the midst of the Peloponnese. In the same hut, in which today I spend the night, I once stayed, when, still almost a boy, I traversed these regions with Adamas. How I sat there so happily on the bench before the house and harkened to the sounds of the distantly approaching caravans and the plashing of the nearby fountain, which under blossoming acacias poured its silver waters into the basin.

Now I am happy once more. I wander through this land, as through Dodona's Grove, where the oaks resounded with glorious prophetic judgements. I see only deeds, past, future, when I also from morning until evening wander beneath the clear Heavens. Believe me, he who travels through this land, and still tolerates a yoke on his shoulders, will be no Pelopidas, he is heartless, or he lacks understanding.

So long it slept — so long the time slid by like the infernal river, dull and silent, in empty idleness?

And yet everything lies ready. Full of avengeful strength are the mountain people round here, lie there like a silent storm cloud that just waits for the great gale, that will drive it. Diotima! let me breathe the breath of God into them, let me speak a word from the heart to them, Diotima! Fear nothing! They will not be so uncivilised. I know raw nature. It scorns reason, but it stands in alliance with enthusiasm. He who just acts with his whole soul, errs never. He does not need to brood, for no power is against him.

HYPERION TO DIOTIMA

Tomorrow I shall be with Alabanda. It is delight for me to enquire the way to Coron, and I ask more often than is necessary. I would like to take on the wings of the Sun and go to him and yet also I linger so gladly and ask: how will he be?

The regal youth! why was I born later? why did I not spring

from One cradle with him? I cannot bear the difference that is between us. O why did I live in Tenos like an idle shepherd boy, and only dreamt of his like, when he was already testing Nature in lively employment and was already wrestling with Sea and Air and all the elements? was there not then in me the urge for glorious deeds as well?

But I will make up for it, I will be quick. By Heaven! I am overripe for deeds. My soul will only rage against itself, if I do not through a vital occupation soon free myself.

Sublime maiden! how could I hold my own before you? How was it possible for you to love such an inactive being?

HYPERION TO DIOTIMA

I have him, belovèd Diotima!

Light is my breast and swift are my sinews, ha! and the future entices me, as clear water depths entice us, to leap in and cool the high-spirited blood in the refreshing bath. But that is babble. We are dearer to one another, than ever, my Alabanda and I. We are freer with each other and yet there is all the fullness and depth of life, as before.

O how right the old Tyrants were, to forbid friendships, such as ours! Then one is strong like a Demigod and tolerates nothing unconscionable within his sphere! —

It was evening, when I entered his room. He had just put aside his work, was sitting in a moonlit corner by the window and was in his thoughts. I stood in darkness, he did not recognise me, looked unconcernedly towards me. Heaven knows for whom he took me.

Well, how are things? he cried. Passable! I said. But the deception was in vain. My voice was full of secret exultation. What is that? he started up; is it you? Yes indeed, you blind one! I cried, and flew into his arms. O now! cried Alabanda at last, now it shall be different, Hyperion!

That I can imagine, I said and shook his hand joyfully.

Do you still know me then, continued Alabanda after a while, have you still got the old innocent belief in Alabanda? Generous one! things have never gone so well for me meanwhile, as when I felt myself to be in the light of your love.

What? I cried, this asks Alabanda? That was not spoken arrogantly, Alabanda. But it is a sign of these times, that the old heroic nature goes begging for respect, and the living human heart, like an orphan, worries itself over a drop of love.

Dear youth! he cried; I have just become old. The lax life everywhere and the affair with the old people, to whom I wanted to take you for schooling in Smyrna —

O it is bitter, I cried; also upon this one, the Goddess of Death ventured, the nameless, that one calls Fate.

Light was brought and we looked at each other anew with gentle loving inquiry. The aspect of the dear one had become very different since the days of hope. Like the midday Sun from the pale sky, his great, ever-vital eyes twinkled at me from a faded face.

Good one! cried Alabanda with friendly reluctance, as I thus regarded him, desist from the melancholy looks, good youth! I know well, I have declined. O my Hyperion! I yearn so much for something great and true and I hope to find it with you. You have grown beyond me, you are freer and stronger, than before and see!

that pleases me heartily. I am the parched land and you come like an auspicious storm — O it is glorious that you are here!

Quiet! I said, you rob me of my senses, and we should not speak of ourselves at all until we are in life, in the midst of deeds.

Yes indeed! cried Alabanda joyfully, only when the hunting horn sounds, do the hunters come alive.

Will it soon begin then? I said.

It will, cried Alabanda, and I say to you, courage! it will be quite a bombardment. Ha! may it extend to the top of the tower and melt its colours and rage and surge round it, until it cracks and falls! — but just do not strike our allies. I know well, the good Russians would gladly use us as firearms. But let that be! when once our powerful Spartans have had the opportunity, to find out who they are, and what they can do, and when we have thus conquered the Peloponnese, then we can laugh in the face of the North Pole and build ourselves a proper life.

A life of our own, I cried, a new, an honourable life. Are we then like a will-o'-the-wisp born in the swamp or do we come from the victors at Salamis? How is it then, now? how then have you become a maidservant, Greek free nature? how have you so fallen, paternal race, of whom the divine images of Jupiter and Apollo were once only a copy? — But hear me, Heaven of Ionia! hear me Earth of the native land, I will no longer tolerate it that, half-naked like a beggar woman, you wrap yourself in the rags of your ancient glory!

O Sun, that reared us! cried Alabanda, you shall witness how with work our courage grows, as beneath the blows of Fate our plan takes shape, like the iron beneath the hammer.

Each inflamed the other.

And that only no stain should remain, I cried, no farce with which, like the rabble the walls, the century could daub us! O, cried Alabanda, therefore also, war is so good —

Right, Alabanda, I cried, as with all great work, where there is man's strength and spirit, and no helping crutch and no waxen wing. Then we lay aside the slaves' clothing on which Fate has impressed us its arms —

Then nothing vain or enforced matters any more, cried Alabanda, then we go unadorned to our goal, without fetters, naked, as in the games at Nemea.

To the goal, I cried, where the new free state dawns and the Pantheon of all the Beautiful rises out of the Greek Earth.

Alabanda was silent for a while. A new flush came into his face, and his form grew, like the refreshed plant, into the heights.

O youth! youth! cried he, then I will drink from your source, then I will live and love. I am very joyful, Heaven of Night, he continued, as though intoxicated, while he went to the window, like vine leaves you arch over me, and like grapes, your stars hang down.

HYPERION TO DIOTIMA

I am fortunate to be fully in the midst of work. I could fall into one folly after another, my soul is so full, the man so intoxicates me, the wonderful, the proud, who loves nothing but me and all humility, that is in him, heaps only on me. O Diotima! this Alabanda has wept before me, has, like a child, prayed to me for atonement, for what he did to me in Smyrna.

118

Who am I then, you dear ones, that I call you mine, that I may say they are my own, that I, like a conqueror, stand between you and, like my spoils, embrace you.

O Diotima! O Alabanda! noble, calmly great beings! how can I achieve if I will not flee from my happiness, from you?

Even as I wrote, I received your letter, you Love.

Grieve not, lovely being, grieve not! Keep yourself, safe from sorrow, for the coming festivals of the native land! Diotima! the glowing Festival of Nature, for that keep yourself and all the bright honorary days of the Gods!

Do you not see Greece already?

O do you not see how, joyful at the new proximity, the eternal stars smile over our cities and groves, how the old Sea, when it sees our people strolling on the shore, remembers again the beautiful Athenians and again brings us fortune, as then its loved ones, on joyful waves?

Soulful maiden! you are so beautiful now! how then, when the real climate nourishes you, you will flourish in enchanting glory!

DIOTIMA TO HYPERION

Most of the time since you went away, I had shut myself in, dear Hyperion! Today I was once more outside.

In lovely February air I have gathered life and bring what I have gathered to you. It has also done me good again, the fresh warmth of the Sky, again I have felt at one with the new wonder of the plant world, the pure, ever-the-same, where all mourns and again rejoices in its own time.

Hyperion! O my Hyperion! why then do we also not walk along the quiet paths of life? They are holy names, Winter and Spring and Summer and Autumn! we, however, know them not. Is it not a sin, to mourn in the Spring? why, nevertheless, do we do it?

Forgive me! the children of the Earth live through the Sun alone; I live through you, I have other joys, is it then a wonder that I have other mourning? and must I mourn? must I then?

Brave one! dear one! should I wilt, if you shine? ought my heart to grow weary if the joy of victory awakens in all your sinews? If, in times past, I had heard that a Greek youth had set out to draw the good people from their humiliation, to bring them again to the maternal beauty, from which they came, how I would have arisen, astounded, from the dream of childhood and thirsted after the image of the dear one? and now he is there, now he is mine, I can still weep? O foolish maiden! is it then not true? is he not the glorious one, and is he not mine! O you shades of blessèd time! you my trusted memories!

It is indeed to me, as though it were hardly yesterday, that magical evening, when the holy stranger for the first time met me, as he, like a mourning Genius, shone into the shadows of the grove, where, in the dream of youth, the carefree maiden sat — in the May air he came, in Ionia's magical May air and it made him more blooming to me, it enticed his hair, unfolded, like flowers, his lips, dissolved into smiles the yearning, and O you beams of Heaven! how you shone on me from out of these eyes, out of these intoxicating Springs where, in the shade of a sheltering arch, eternal life shimmers and moves! —

Good gods! how beautiful he became as he gazed at me! how

the whole youth, a span taller, stood there, lightly nerved, only that his dear arms, the shy ones, sank down as though they were nothing! and how he looked up in rapture as though I had escaped to Heaven and were no more there, ah! how he then in all sweetness of heart smiled and blushed, as he again became aware of me and, through his darkening tears, his Phoebus eye beamed in order to ask, is it you? is it really you?

And why did he meet me with such devout mind, so full of dear superstition? why had he first sunk his head, why was the divine youth so full of yearning and sorrow? His Genius was too blissful to remain alone, and the world too poor to comprehend him. O it was a dear picture, interwoven with greatness and suffering! But now it is otherwise! suffering is at an end! He has something to do, he is the invalid no more! —

I was full of sighs when I began to write to you, my beloved! Now I am pure joy. Thus speaking of you, one speaks oneself into happiness. And see! so shall it also remain. Farewell!

HYPERION TO DIOTIMA

We have still celebrated your festival to a good conclusion, dear Life! before the clamour begins. It was a heavenly day. The lovely early year drifted and gleamed from the Orient, conjured your name from us, as it conjures the blossom from the trees, and all the blessèd secrets of love breathed out of me. A love, like ours, my friend had never witnessed, and it was charming, how the proud man attended and his eye and spirit was ardent to comprehend your image, your being.

O, he cried finally, then it is well worth the effort, to fight for our Greece, if it still bears such growth!

Yes, indeed, my Alabanda, I said; then we go cheerfully into combat, then divine fire drives us to deeds, when our spirit is so rejuvenated by the image of such natures, and then one does not run after a petty goal, one doesn't worry about this and that, and regardless of the spirit, superficially elaborate and, for the sake of the goblet, drink the wine; we will only rest then, Alabanda, when the wonder of the Genius is a secret no longer, only then when the eyes all turn into triumphal arches, where the Spirit of mankind, the long absent, shines forth out of the wrongs and suffering and, victoriously joyful, greets the paternal Aether. — Ha! from the colours alone no one shall recognise our future people; everything must grow young again, it must be fundamentally different; full of seriousness and pleasure and cheerful all work! nothing, not even the smallest, the most commonplace, without the Spirit and the Gods! Love and Hate and every tone from us must estrange the meaner world and also no moment may once remind us of the vulgar past!

HYPERION TO DIOTIMA

The volcano erupts. In Coron and Modon the Turks are besieged and we move with our mountain folk up towards the Peloponnese.

Now all melancholy is at an end, Diotima, and my spirit is firmer and swifter since I am in active work and see! I also now have an ordered day.

With the Sun I begin. Then I go out, to where in the shade of the woods my war folk are quartered, and greet the thousand bright eyes, that then look up to me in wild friendliness. An awakened army! I know nothing like it and all life in towns and villages is, in comparison, like a swarm of bees.

Man cannot deny, that he was once happy, like the stag of the forest; and after countless years there still rises in us a yearning for the days of the primæval world, where each strode the Earth like a God, before, I know not what? made men tame, and still, instead of walls and dead wood, the Soul of the World, the holy omnipresent Air, surrounded him.

Diotima! it is often to me wonderful, when I walk through my carefree folk and, as though grown out of the earth, one after another gets up and stretches himself towards the morning light, and amongst the crowd of men the crackling flames rise up, where the mother sits with the freezing little child, where the refreshing food is cooking, whilst the horses, scenting the day, snort and whinny, and the woods resound with the concussive war music, and all around weapons gleam and rustle — but those are words and the real joy of such a life cannot be told.

Then my company joyfully gather round me, and it is wonderful, how also the oldest and most obstinate honour me in all my youth. We become more trusting and many relate, how his life has been and my heart is often full of many a fate. Then I begin, to talk of better days, and their eyes open and shine, when they think of the covenant, that shall be ours, and the splendid picture of the coming free state dawns before them.

All for each and each for all! There is a joyful spirit in the words and it also always grips my men, like a commandment of the Gods.

O Diotima! to thus see how, with hopes there, the obstinate nature softens and all her pulses beat more powerfully and with plans the darkened brow clears and shines, to thus stand there in a circle of men, surrounded by belief and desire, that is indeed more, than seeing Earth and Sky and Sea in all their glory.

Then I drill them in arms and marching until midday. The joyful state of mind makes them teachable, as it makes me into the master. One moment they stand closely ranked in Macedonian file and move only their arms, the next, in individual groups, they fly apart like shafts to a more daring combat, where the pliant strength changes with every position and each is his own commander-in-chief, and assemble themselves again at a safe point — and always where they go and stand in such a dance of weapons, there hovers before their and my eyes the image of the servants of tyranny and the more serious battle field.

Thereupon, when the sun shines more fiercely, council is held in the depths of the woods and it is a joy, thus with quiet senses to hold sway over the great future. We take the power from chance, we master Fate. We allow resistance to arise according to our will, we incite the enemy to that, for which we are armed. Or we look on and appear afraid and let him come nearer, until he offers us his total defeat, likewise we quickly confuse him and that is my panacea. But the more learnèd doctors do not think much of such sovereign remedies.

How good then are the evenings for me with my Alabanda, when, for pleasure, we go around the sun-red hills on lively horses, and on to the peaks, where we linger, the air playing in our animals' manes, and the friendly rustling entering into our conversation, whilst we look out into the distances of Sparta, that are our war prize! and then when we are back and sitting together in the lovely cool of the night, where the goblet is fragrant and the moonlight shines on our frugal meal and in the midst of our smiling quietness the history of the ancients, rises like a cloud from the holy ground, that bears us, how blessèd it is there in such a moment to offer each other one's hand!

Then Alabanda would probably speak further of many a one, who is plagued by the tediousness of the century, of so many wonderful crooked ways, that life forges for itself, since its straight path has been blocked, then I also think of my Adamas, with his journeys, his particular longing to be in the depths of Asia — those are just expedients, good old one! I would then cry to him, come! and build your world! with us! for our world is also yours.

Also yours, Diotima, for it is a copy of yourself. O you, with your Elysium stillness, if only we could create, what you are!

HYPERION TO DIOTIMA

We have now triumphed three times in succession in small engagements, but where the combatants ran through one another, like lightning, and everything was one consuming flame. Navarin is ours and we are now at the stronghold of Mistra, the remains of Ancient Sparta. I have also set the flag, that I snatched from an Albanian horde, upon a ruin, that lies before the city, and joyfully thrown my Turkish headband into the Eurotas and wear since then the Greek helmet.

And now I would like to see you, O maiden! I would like to see you and take your hands and press them to my heart, for which the joy will perhaps soon be too great! soon! in a week perhaps it will be freed, the ancient, noble, holy Peloponnese.

O then, you dear one! teach me to be devout! then teach my overflowing heart a prayer! I should be quiet, for what have I done? and had I done something, of which I would like to speak, how much yet remains? But what can I do, if my thought is faster than the time? I would so gladly, that it were otherwise and time and action flew beyond thoughts and winged victory outran hope itself.

My Alabanda blossoms, like a bridegroom. From each one of his glances the coming world laughs at me, and this to some extent stills my impatience.

Diotima! I would not exchange this coming happiness for the most beautiful age of Ancient Greece, and the smallest of our victories is dearer to me, than Marathon and Thermopylae and Plataea. Is it not true? Is not recovering life of more worth to the heart, than the unalloyed, that yet knows not illness? Only when youth is gone, do we love it, and only then when, the lost returns, does it make happy all depths of the soul.

By the Eurotas stands my tent, and when after midnight I awaken, the old River God murmurs admonishingly past me, and smiling I take the flowers of the bank, and strew them in his shining waters and say to him: take it as a sign, you lonely one! Soon the old life will blossom around you again.

DIOTIMA TO HYPERION

I have received the letters, my Hyperion, that you wrote to me on the way. You move me strongly with everything you say to me, and in the midst of my love I often shudder, to see the gentle youth, who wept at my feet, changed into this armed being.

Will you not then forget what you have learnt of Love?

But just continue to change! I will follow you. I believe, if you could hate me, I would even there then appreciate and assimilate your mood, would take pains, to hate you and then our souls would remain equal and that is no vain exaggeration, Hyperion.

I myself am also completely different, from usual. I lack the serene view of the world and the spontaneous joy in all living things. Only the realm of the Stars still attracts my eye. And, in return, I muse all the more dearly on the great spirits of antiquity and how they have ended on Earth, and the noble Spartan women have won my heart. At the same time I do not forget the new warriors, the strong, whose hour has come, often I hear their noise of victory roaring towards me through the Peloponnese nearer and nearer, often I see them, surging down like a cataract, through the Epidaurian woods and from the distance their weapons gleaming in the light of the Sun, that, like a herald, leads them, O my Hyperion! and you come quickly over to Calaurea and greet the quiet woods of our love, greet me, and then fly back again to your task; — and do you think, I fear the outcome? Dearest! sometimes it almost overcomes me, but my greater thoughts, like flames, hold off the frost. —

Farewell! fulfil as the spirit has commanded you! and for the sake of Peace, do not let the war last too long, Hyperion, for the sake of the beautiful, new, golden Peace, when, as you say, one day the rules of Nature will be written in our law book, and where life itself, where she, divine Nature, which cannot be written down in any book, will be in the heart of the community. Farewell.

HYPERION TO DIOTIMA

You should have calmed me, my Diotima! should have said I ought not to act rashly, ought not gradually extort victory from Fate like a sum from miserly debtors. O maiden! to stand still is worse than anything. My blood dries in my veins, I so thirst to advance, and have to stay here idle, must besiege and besiege from one day to the next. Our folk want to take by storm, but that would inflame their excited feelings to the point of intoxication and woe then to our hopes, if the savage being arises and rends apart discipline and love.

I do not know, it could last only a few days more, then Mistra must surrender, but I would that we were further. In the camp here it is to me, as in thundery air. I am impatient, also my men do not please me. There is a terrible wantonness amongst them.

But it is not wise of me to make so much of my mood. And Ancient Lacedæmon is indeed worth one's suffering a little anxiety before one has it.

HYPERION TO DIOTIMA

It is finished, Diotima! our people have plundered, murdered indiscriminately, our brothers are also slain, the Greeks in Mistra, the innocents, or they wander helplessly about and their dead lamenting expressions cry to Heaven and Earth for revenge on the barbarians at whose head I was.

Now can I go forth and preach about my good cause. O now all hearts fly to me!

But I have also acted cleverly. I knew my people. Indeed! it was an extraordinary project, to found my Elysium with a gang of robbers.

No! by holy Nemesis! it serves me right and I will also bear it, bear it I will, until the pain finally severs my consciousness from me.

Do you think I rave? I have a respectable wound, which one of my faithful gave me, whilst I was warding off the outrage. When I was delirious, I would rip the bandage from it and then the blood would run to where it belonged, in this grieving Earth.

This grieving Earth! the naked! that I so wanted to clothe with holy groves, so wanted to adorn with all the flowers of Greek life.

O it would have been beautiful, my Diotima.

Do you call me spiritless? Dear maiden! it is too great a disaster. At all extremities furious hordes are breaking in; like a pestilence, rapacity rages in Morea and he who does not take up a sword, is driven away, slaughtered and thereby, say the raving ones, they are fighting for our freedom. More of the brutal people have been drafted in by the Sultan and carry on, like the others.

I have just heard, that our dishonourable army is now scattered. Near Tripoli the cowards met an Albanian horde, which was smaller in number by half. But because there was nothing to plunder, the wretched men all ran away. The Russians who ventured on the campaign with us, forty good men, alone held out, but all met their death.

And so I am now with my Alabanda again alone, as before. Since the loyal man saw me fall and bleed in Mistra, he has forgotten all else, his hopes, his desire for victory, his despair. The furious one, who fell amongst the plunderers, like a punishing God, then led me so gently out of the tumult, and his tears moistened my garments. He also stayed with me in the hut, where since then I have lain and am now really happy about it. For had he moved on with them, he would be now lying in the dust near Tripoli.

How it will progress, I do not know. Fate drives me out into the unknown and I have deserved it; from you, my own shame banishes me and who knows, how long?

Ah! I have promised you a Greece and you receive now instead a lament. Be yourself your comfort!

HYPERION TO DIOTIMA

I bring myself to words with difficulty.

It is pleasing to speak, one chatters away like the birds as long as the world, like the air of May, breathes about one; but between midday and evening it can become otherwise and what is lost in the end?

Believe me and reflect, I say it to you from my deepest soul: language is a great superfluity. The best abides always for itself and stays in its profundity, like the pearl in the depths of the sea. — But what I really wanted to write to you, because, indeed, some time the painting must have its frame and man his daily task, so then I will serve still for a while, in the Russian fleet; for with the Greeks I have nothing further to do.

O dear maiden! it has become very dark about me!

HYPERION TO DIOTIMA

I have temporized, struggled. But finally it must be.

I see what is necessary, and because I see it, so it must be. Do not misunderstand me! do not condemn me! I must advise you to leave me, my Diotima.

I am nothing for you any more, you lovely being! This heart is dried up for you, and my eyes see the living no more. O my lips are parched; the sweet breath of love wells up in my bosom no more.

One day has taken all youth from me; by the Eurotas my life has wept itself weary, ah! by the Eurotas, who in helpless humiliation flowed past, lamenting with all his waves the ruins of Lacedaemon. There, there has Fate finished reaping me. — Should I keep your love like a charity? — I am so nothing, am so obscure, like the poorest knave. I am banished, accursed like a common rebel and in the future many a Greek in Morea will relate to his children's children our heroic deeds, like a tale of robbers.

Ah! and one thing I have long concealed from you. Ceremoniously my father cast me off, banished me without return, from the house of my youth, does not wish to see me again, not in this, or the other life, as he says. Thus read the answer to the letter, in which I wrote to him of my undertaking.

But do not now allow compassion to lead you astray. Believe me, throughout there still remains for us a joy. Real pain inspires. He who steps upon his misery, stands higher. And that is glorious, that not until we suffer do we fully feel the freedom of the soul. Freedom! who understands the word — it is a profound word, Diotima. I am so inwardly assailed, am so shockingly insulted, am without hope, without a goal, am totally without honour, and yet there is a power within me, invincible, that permeates my body with a sweet thrill, each time I stir.

Also I have my Alabanda still. He has as little to gain, as I. Him I can keep for myself without harm. Ah! the regal youth should have merited a better lot. He has become so mild and so quiet. That often nearly breaks my heart. But one supports the other. We say nothing to each other; what should we say? but there is, however, a blessing in many a little kindness we perform for each other.

There he sleeps and smiles contentedly, in the midst of our fate. The good one! he does not know what I do. He would not tolerate it. You must write to Diotima, he ordered me, and must say to her, that she must soon get ready to flee with you, into a tolerable country. But he does not know, that a heart that has so learnt to despair, like his and mine, is nothing more to the belovèd. No! no! you would never find peace with Hyperion, you would have to be unfaithful and that I wish to spare you.

And so farewell then, you sweet maiden! farewell! I would like to say to you, go hither, go thither; there rush the Springs of life. I would like to show you a free land, a land full of beauty and full of soul and say: thither save yourself! But O Heaven, could I do this, then I would be another and then I would not have to bid you farewell — bid farewell? Ah! I know not what I do. I imagined myself so composed, so collected. Now I am dizzy and my heart tosses about, like an impatient invalid. Woe is me! I am destroying my last joy. But it must be and the Alas! of Nature is here in vain. I owe it to you, and, moreover, I was born to be homeless and without a resting place. O Earth! O you Stars! will I live nowhere at all in the end?

Just once more I would like to return to your breast, wherever it would be! Aetherial eyes! Just once more meet myself in you! hang on your lips, you lovely one! you ineffable one! and drink in your charming heavenly-sweet life — but do not listen to that! I pray you, do not heed it! I would say I were a seducer, if you listened. You know me, you understand me. You know, how highly you esteem me if you do not pity me, do not hear me.

I can, I may no more — how has the priest a mind to live, when his God is no more there? O Genius of my people! O Soul of Greece! I must go down, I must seek you in the realm of the dead.

HYPERION TO DIOTIMA

I have long waited, I have to confess, I have longingly hoped for a parting word from your heart, but you are silent. Also that is a language of your beautiful soul, Diotima.

Is it not true, the more holy accords do not therefore cease? is it not true, Diotima, that when the soft moonlight of love sinks down, the higher Stars of its Heaven always still shine? O that is my final joy, that we are inseparable, even if no sound from you to me, no shadow of our blessèd days of youth return!

I look out into the sunset glowing Sea, I stretch my arms out to the place, where far away you live and my soul warms once again with all the joys of love and youth.

O Earth! my cradle! all bliss and all pain is in the parting that we take from you.

You dear islands of Ionia! and you, my Calaurea, and you, my Tenos, you are all there before me, as distant as you are and my

Spirit flies with the zephyrs over the moving waters; and you who, to my side, grow dusky, you shores of Teos and Ephesus, where once with Alabanda I walked in the days of hope, you appear again to me, as then, and I would like to take a ship over to the land and kiss the ground and warm the ground upon my breast, and stammer all sweet words of parting to the silent Earth, before I fly up into liberty.

Pity, pity, that it is now no better amongst men, gladly, otherwise, I would remain upon this goodly star. But I can do without this globe, that is more, than all, that it can give.

Let us in the Sunlight, O child! endure bondage, said the mother to Polyxena, and her love of life could not speak more beautifully. But it is just the Sunlight, that dissuades me from slavery, that does not allow me to remain on the dishonoured Earth, and the holy beams attract me like paths that lead to home.

For a long time the majesty of the fateless soul has been more present to me, than all other; in glorious solitude I have sometimes lived within myself; I have become accustomed, to shake off external things like flakes of snow; how should I then shrink, from seeking so-called death? have I not a thousand times freed myself in thought, how should I then hesitate *once* to really do it? Are we then like bonded slaves, tied to ground we plough? are we like tame birds, that dare not venture from the yard because there they are fed?

We are like the young eagle, that the father pushes from the nest, so that it seeks for prey in the high Aether.

Tomorrow our fleet goes to battle and the war will be hot enough. I consider this engagement a bath to wash away the dust; I will most likely find that which I wish; wishes like mine, are easily granted at one's destination. And then, despite all, I would finally have achieved something with my campaign, and see, amongst men no labour is in vain.

Godly soul! I would like to say, remember me, if you should come to my grave. But they will probably throw me into the sea, and I contemplate gladly, how my remains shall there sink, down to where meet all the Springs and Rivers that I loved, and where the storm cloud rises and impregnates the mountains and the valleys, that I loved. And we? O Diotima! Diotima! when shall we see each other again?

It is impossible, and my whole life rebels, if should I think, as though we lose each other. For centuries long I would wander through the Stars, take on all forms, all languages of life, to once again meet you. But I think that which is like, will soon find itself.

Great soul! you will be able to reconcile yourself to this parting and so let me wander! Greet your mother! Greet Notara and the other friends.

Also the Trees greet, where first I met you and the joyful Brooks, where we walked and the beautiful gardens of Angele, and let, you loved one, my image meet you there. Fare well.

SECOND BOOK

HYPERION TO BELLARMIN

I was in a lovely dream, when I copied the letters for you that I once exchanged. Now I write to you again, my Bellarmin! and lead you further down, down into the profoundest depths of my suffering, and then, you last of my loved ones! come with me out to the place where a new day shines upon us.

The battle of which I wrote to Diotima, began. The Turkish ships had fled into the canal, between the island of Chios and the Asiatic coast, and stood by firm ground up by Tschesme. My Admiral left the ranks with his ship, on which I was, and opened up the preliminaries with the leading Turkish ship. The furious pair was immediately with the first offensive worked up into a frenzy. It was a terrible tumult of intoxicated revenge. The ships were soon firmly caught in one another with their rigging; the raging combat became ever closer and closer.

I was still filled with a deep feeling of vitality. I felt warm and well in all my limbs. Like one who is tenderly departing, my spirit was aware in all its senses for the last time and then, full of burning ill-humour that I knew no better, than to allow myself to be slaughtered amongst a crowd of barbarians, with angry tears in my eyes, I stormed in to where my death was certain.

I met close enough with enemy and of the Russians, who fought at my side, there was in few moments not one remaining. I stood alone there, full of pride, and threw my life, like a beggar's penny, before the barbarians, but they did not want me. They looked on me as one whom it was feared to sin against, and Fate appeared to respect me in my despair.

Out of utter self-defence then one charged at me, and struck me, so that I fell. From then on I was conscious of nothing, until I awoke again on Paros whither I had been taken by ship.

From the servant, who carried me out of the battle, I heard afterwards, that both ships that had begun the fight, had gone up in flames, the moment after he with the surgeon had taken me away in a boat. The Russians had thrown a fire brand into the Turkish ship, and because their own hung fast to the other, it burnt up with it.

The outcome of this terrible battle is known to you. Thus one venom punishes the other, I cried when I learnt the Russians had set fire to the whole Turkish fleet — thus the tyrants exterminate themselves.

HYPERION TO BELLARMIN

Six days after the battle I lay in a painful death-like sleep. My life was, like a night, interrupted by pain like flashing lightning. The first, that I recognised again, was Alabanda. He had, as I learnt, not stirred from me for a moment, had, practically on his own, attended me, with inconceivable zeal, with a thousand tender homely deeds, of which, in life, he otherwise never thought, and he had been heard crying on his knees by my bed: O live, my dear! that I may live!

It was a joyful awakening, Bellarmin! when my eye then again opened to the light, and with tears of reunion the glorious one stood before me.

I offered him my hand and the proud one kissed it with all the rapture of love. He lives, he cried, O saviour! O Nature! you, good, all-healing! your poor pair, the homeless, the errant, you still do not desert! O I will never forget it, Hyperion! how before my eyes, your ship burnt up, and, thundering, drew the sailors with it into the raging flames, and amongst the few saved there was no Hyperion. I was out of my mind and the furious noise of battle did not calm me. But soon I had tidings of you and flew after you, as soon as we were completely finished with the enemy. —

And how he then cared for me! how with loving care he held me prisoner in the magic circle of his kindnesses! how he, without a word, with his great calm taught me, to boldly and unenviously, understand the full scope of the world!

O you sons of the Sun! you freer souls! much has been lost with this Alabanda. I sought in vain and implored life, since he has gone; such a Roman nature I have never found. The carefree, the profoundly wise one, the brave, the noble! Where is a man if it were not he? And when he was friendly and patient, then it was, as when the evening light plays in the darkness of the majestic oak and its leaves drip from the storm of the day.

HYPERION TO BELLARMIN

It was in the lovely days of Autumn, that, half recovered from my wound, I went to my window for the first time. I came with a quieter mind once more in life and my soul had become more attentive. With its most gentle magic Heaven breathed on me, and mildly, like a shower of petals, the clear sunbeams streamed down. There was a great, still, tender spirit in this season, and the calm of consummation, the wonder of maturity in the branches and rustling leaves surrounded me, like the renewed youth, that the ancients hoped for in their Elysium.

I had for a long time not experienced with pure soul, the child-like life of the world, now my eye opened with all the joy of reunion and blessèd Nature had remained changeless in her beauty. My tears flowed before her like an offering of atonement and, shudder-ing, a new heart rose out of the old ill-humour. O holy plant world! I cried, we strive and scheme and yet have you! we struggle with mortal strength to build something beautiful, and yet carefree, it grows up beside us! is it not true, Alabanda? man is made to worry about need, the rest is sufficient unto itself. And yet — I cannot forget how much more I wanted.

Let it suffice you, dear! that you are, cried Alabanda, and do not any more disturb your quiet working through your grief.

I also wish to rest, I said. O I would like to tear up all the plans, the demands, like promissory notes. I wish to keep myself pure, as an artist keeps himself, you will I love, inoffensive life, life of the Groves and the Springs! you will I honour, O Sunlight! soothe myself with you, beautiful Aether that inspires the Stars, and here also breathes around these trees and here touches us in the depths of our breast! O wilfulness of man! like a beggar, I have bowed my head and the silent Gods of Nature with all their gifts perceived it! — You smile, Alabanda? O how often in our early days, you have thus smiled, when your boy chatted away before you, with the intoxicated courage of youth, whilst you stood there, like a still temple pillar, stood, in the ruins of the world, and had to suffer, the wild tendrils of my love to grow round you — see! like a bandage it falls from my eyes and the ancient golden days are alive here once more.

Ah! he cried, this earnestness, in which we lived and this lust for life!

When we hunted in the forest, I cried, when we bathed ourselves in the waters of the Sea, when we sang and drank, where, through the shadows of the laurel, the Sun and the wine and eyes and lips gleamed for us — it was a unique life and our spirit shone like a shining heaven, around our youthful happiness. Therefore also neither allows the other to part, said Alabanda.

O I have a serious confession to lay before you, I said. Will you believe me, that I had wanted to go away? from you? that I violently sought my death! was that not heartless? mad? ah and my Diotima! she should leave me, I wrote to her, and after that another letter, the evening before the battle — and there you wrote, he cried, that you wanted to find your end in the battle? O Hyperion! But she probably has not yet received the last letter. You must only hasten, to write to her that you live.

Best Alabanda! I cried, that is comfort! I will write immediately and send my servant forth with it. O I will offer him all, that I have, so that he hastens and still gets to Calaurea in time. —

And the other letter, in which you spoke of renunciation, of course the good soul will readily forgive, he added.

Will she forgive? I cried; O all you hopes! yes! if I could still be happy with the angel!

140

You will still be happy, cried Alabanda; the most beautiful time of life is still before you. A hero is the youth, a God the man, if he can live to see it.

It grew wonderfully lighter in my soul with his words.

The treetops shivered softly; like flowers out of the dark Earth, the Stars sprang out of the womb of the night and Heaven's Spring shone on me in holy joy.

HYPERION TO BELLARMIN

A few moments later, just when I was about to write to Diotima, Alabanda came joyfully into the room again. A letter, Hyperion! he cried; I was seized with terror and flew to him.

How long, wrote Diotima, I had to live without a sign from you! You wrote to me about the fateful days in Mistra and I replied quickly; but it would seem that you did not receive my letter. You wrote to me again soon after, brief and melancholy, and said to me that you were intending to go into the Russian Fleet; I answered again; yet also this letter you did not receive; now I have also waited in vain, from May until now, the end of the Summer, until a few days ago the letter came, that told me I must renounce you, dear!

You have counted on me, believed me capable of not being insulted by this letter. That pleased me deeply, in the midst of my distress.

Unhappy, great spirit! I have understood you only too well. O it is so completely natural, that you want never to love, because your greater wishes languish. Must you then not scorn the food, when you are about to die of thirst?

141

I knew it early on; I could not be everything to you. Could I loosen the bonds of mortality for you? could I appease the flame in your breast for which no Spring flows and no vine grows? could I offer you the joys of the world in one vessel?

That is what you want. That is what you need and you cannot be otherwise. The boundless impotency of your contemporaries has killed you.

Who once, thus, like you, has been so insulted in his whole soul, he rests no more in isolated joy, who thus, like you, has so experienced stale nothingness, lights up only in the sublime spirit, who so experienced death, as you, recovers only amongst the Gods.

Lucky are all those who do not understand you! He who understands you, must share your greatness and your despair.

I found you, as you are. The primary curiosity of life drove me to the wonderful being. Ineffably, the tender soul attracted me and, childishly fearless, I played about your dangerous flame. — The beautiful joys of our love soothed you; wilful man! only, to make you more impetuous. They soothed, they comforted me also, they made me forget, that you basically were inconsolable, and that I also was not far from becoming so, since seeing into your belovèd heart.

In Athens, amongst the ruins of Olympieum it moved me anew. I had otherwise, probably in a light moment thought, that the youth's mourning was not so serious and inexorable. It is so seldom, that a person with the first step into life, all at once, in such minute detail, so quickly, so deeply experiences the whole fate of his time, and that it ineradicably clings to him, this feeling, because he is not harsh enough, to drive it out, and not weak enough, to weep it out, that, my dearest! is so seldom, that it appears to us almost unnatural.

Then, in the rubble of bright Athens, then I myself was too much grieved to the heart how the tables had turned, so that now, above, the dead walk over the Earth and the living, the divine men, are below, then I saw it all too literally and too actually written on your face, then I acknowledged the rightness of your views for ever. But at the same time you appeared to me greater. A being full of secret power, full of undeveloped significance, a unique hopeful youth you seemed to me. He to whom Fate speaks so audibly, he may speak more audibly with Fate, I said to myself; the more unfathomably he suffers, the more unfathomably powerful he is. From you, from you only, I hoped for all recovery. I saw you travel, I saw you act. O the transformation! Founded by you, the Grove of Academia was in leaf once more above the hearkening pupils, and, as once, the divine discourses were heard again by the Maple of Ilissus.

The Genius of our youth soon won in your school the seriousness of the ancients, and his transitory games became more immortal, for he was ashamed, considered the butterfly flight to be imprisonment. —

For him a horse, would have been enough to master; now he is a general. All too satisfied he would have sung an idle song; now he is an artist. For the powers of the hero, the powers of the world you had disclosed to them in open combat; the riddle of your heart you had given them to solve; thus learnt the youths to reconcile the great, learnt to understand the play of Nature, the soulful, and forgot the raillery. — Hyperion! Hyperion! have you not made me, a minor, into a muse? Thus it was as well with the others.

Ah! now they did not so easily forsake one another, the sociable people; no more, like the sand in the storm of the wilderness, did they erringly wander amongst one another, or youth and age laugh at itself, or the stranger lack a host and the fellow countrymen nevermore separated from one another; and all the lovers never again lost pleasure in each other; at your source, Nature, they refreshed themselves, ah! with the holy joys that mysteriously well from your depths and renew the spirit; and the Gods enlivened once more the fadeable soul of man; the heart- preserving Gods kept each friendly union amongst them. For you, Hyperion, had healed the eye of your Greeks, so that they saw the vitality of life, and that which slept in them, like fire in wood, enthusiasm you had kindled, so that they felt the quiet, constant inspiration of Nature and her pure children. Ah! now men did not take the world any more as the layman the poem of the artist, when they praise the words and perceive therein its utility. A magical example you were, living Nature, to the Greeks, and, kindled by the ever-youthful joy of the Gods, all human activity was, as once, a festival; and, more beautiful than war music, the young heroes were led to deeds by Helios's light.

Hush! hush! It was my most beautiful dream, my first and my last. You are too proud, to occupy yourself any longer with the villainous race. You are also right in this. You led them to freedom and they thought on robbery. You lead them triumphantly into their ancient Lacedæmonia and these monsters plunder and you are cursed by your father, great son! and no wilderness, no cave is safe enough for you on this Greek soil, that you, like a shrine, revered, that you, more than me, loved.

O my Hyperion! I am no longer the mild maiden any more,

since knowing all this. Anger drives me upwards, so that I hardly like to look to Earth and unceasingly my insulted heart trembles.

We should part. You are right. Also I do not want children; for I do not wish for them the world of slavery, and indeed the poor plants would fade away before my eyes in this aridness.

Fare well! you dear youth! go thither where it seems to you to be worthwhile to surrender your soul. The world probably still has a battlefield, a place of sacrifice, where you can acquit yourself. It would be a pity if all the good powers, like a vision, thus passed away. Yet however you make an end, you turn to the Gods, return into the holy, free, youthful life of Nature from whence you came, and that is indeed your only desire and also mine.

Thus she wrote to me. I was shattered to the core, full of terror and joy, but I sought to control myself to find words to answer.

You consent, Diotima? I wrote, you sanction my renunciation? can understand it? — Faithful soul! you could be reconciled to it? Also to my darkest error you could be reconciled, heavenly patience! and would sacrifice yourself, obscure yourself out of love, happy darling of Nature! and become like me, and by your assent sanctify my grief? Beautiful heroine! which crown did you earn?

But now enough of mourning, you love! You have followed me in my night, now come! and let me follow you to your light, to your grace let us return, beautiful heart! O your calm let me see again, blessèd Nature! before your image of peace let my arrogance for ever pass away from me.

It is true, is it not, you Dear One! my return is still not too late, and you will take me again and can love me again as before? it is true, the joy of our past days is still not for us lost?

I have pushed things to extremes. I have acted most unthankfully towards the maternal Earth, have thrown away my blood and all the gifts, she gave me, like a servant's wages and ah! how a thousand times more unthankful to you, you holy maiden! who once took me into her peace, me, a shy torn being, from whose oppressed heart hardly a glimmer of youth stole as here and there a stalk of grass on trodden ways. Had you not called me into life? was I not yours? how could I then — O you do not know of it yet, as I hope, have not yet the unfortunate letter in your hands, that I wrote to you before the last battle? Then I wanted to die, Diotima, and I believed it to be a holy deed. But how can that be holy, which separates lovers? how can that be holy, which shatters our life's devout happiness? — Diotima? beautiful born life! I am now to you, in return, all the more like your intrinsic self, I have finally learnt to esteem it, I have learnt to preserve, what is good and sincere on Earth. O even if I could alight above on the shining islands of Heaven, would I find more than I find with Diotima?

Listen to me now, belovèd!

In Greece I can stay no longer. That you know. On my departure my father sent me as much of his plenty to suffice for us to escape into a holy valley of the Alps or the Pyrenees and there to buy a friendly house and also as much of the green Earth, that is necessary for life's golden mean.

If you are willing, then I will come immediately and with a faithful arm lead you and your mother and we will kiss the shores of Calaurea and dry our tears, and hasten over the Isthmus into the Adriatic Sea, from where a reliable ship will take us further.

O come! in the depths of the mountain world the secret of our hearts will rest, like the jewel in the shaft, in the lap of the heaven-reaching woods, it will be to us as though we were within the pillars of the most inner temple, which the godless do not approach, and we will sit by the Spring, in its mirror look at our world, the sky and house and garden and ourselves. Often in the serene night we will wander in the shade of our orchard and harken to the God in us, the loving, whilst the plant lifts its sunken head from its midday slumber and the quiet life of your flowers coolingly refreshes itself, as they bathe their delicate arms in the dew, and the night Air breathes round and permeates them, and above us blossoms the meadow of Heaven with all its twinkling flowers, and to one side behind westerly clouds the moon shyly, as though out of love, imitates the setting of the Sun Youth, — and then in the morning, when like a river bed our valley fills itself with warm light, and quietly the golden flood runs through our trees, and flows round our house and beautifies for you the lovely rooms, your creation, and you walk in their sunny splendour, and in your grace bless the day for me, love! when then, whilst we thus celebrate the morning's wonder, the Earth's busy life kindles, like a sacrificial fire before our eyes, and we then go forth about our daily work, to also cast our share into the mounting flame, will you not then say, we are happy, we are again like the ancient priests of Nature, the holy and joyful, who were already pious before ever a temple stood.

Have I said enough? decide now my fate, dear maiden, and soon! — It is fortunate, that I am still partly an invalid from the last battle, and have not yet been discharged from service; I could otherwise not stay, I would have to go forth myself, would have to ask, and that would not be good, that would be called assailing you. —

Ah, Diotima! uneasy, foolish thoughts strike my heart and yet — I cannot think that this hope will founder as well.

Have you not then grown too great, to return to the joy of the Earth? does it not consume, the passionate flame of the spirit that has been inflamed by your suffering, does it not consume all mortality in you?

I know well that he who easily falls out with the world, the more easily reconciles himself with it. But you, with your child stillness, you, so happy once in your great humility, Diotima! who will reconcile you, when Fate rouses you to indignation?

Dear life! is there then no more healing power for you in me? of all the sounds of the heart does none call you back into human life, where you once, with lowered wings, so sweetly lingered? O come, O stay in this twilight! For this shadow land is the element of love and here only flows the quiet dew of sadness from the Heaven of your eyes.

And do you not think any more on our golden days? the most lovely, divinely melodious? do they not rustle to you from all the groves of Calaurea?

And see! there is so much perished in me, and I have few hopes more. Your picture with its heavenly import, I still have, like a household God, rescued from the fire. Our life, ours is still undamaged in me. Should I now go forth and bury this as well? Shall I, restless and without a goal, go out from one strange place into another. Have I for that reason learnt love?

O no! you First and you Last! Mine you were, and mine you will remain.

HYPERION TO BELLARMIN

I sat with Alabanda on a hill in the area, in lovely warming sun, and around us the wind played with the fallen leaves. The land was silent; only here and there sounded in the wood a falling tree felled by a peasant, and beside us murmured the fleeting rain stream down into the peaceful sea.

I was to a certain extent carefree; I hoped now to soon see my Diotima, soon now to live with her in quiet happiness. Alabanda had talked me out of all misgivings; so sure about it was he himself. He also was serene; but in another sense. The future had no more power over him. O I knew it not; he was at the end of his happiness, regarded with all his rights, the world, with all his conquering nature useless to him, ineffectual and lonely, and he just let it happen, as though a game played to pass the time had been lost.

Then a messenger came towards us. He brought us our discharge from war service, which we had both asked for in the Russian fleet, because there was nothing more for us to do, that seemed worthwhile. I could now leave Paros, if I wanted to. I was also now well enough for the journey. I did not want to wait for Diotima's answer, wanted to go straight to her, it was as though a God drove me to Calaurea. As Alabanda heard that, his colour changed and he looked at me sadly. So easy it is for my Hyperion, he cried, to leave his Alabanda?

Leave? I cried, how then is that then?

O you dreamers! he cried, do you not then see that we must part?

How should I see it, I replied; you certainly say nothing about it; and what now and then appeared in you, that could indicate departure, I gladly took for whim, for exuberance —

O I know it, he cried, this heavenly game of abundant love, that creates for itself difficulties in order to relieve itself of its riches and I would it were so with me, you good one! but here it is serious!

Serious? I cried, and why then?

Because, my Hyperion, he said softly, because I would not like to disturb your future happiness, because I must fear Diotima's proximity. Believe me, it is dangerous to live around lovers, and an inactive heart, as mine now is, bears it with difficulty.

Ah good Alabanda! I said smiling, how you mistake yourself! you are not so waxen and your constant soul does not so easily leap beyond its bounds. For the first time in your life you are capricious. You act here with me as a sick nurse and one sees how little you are born to it. The sitting still has made you timid —

Do you see? he cried, that is just it. Would I live more actively with you? and if it were another! but this Diotima! can I do otherwise? can I be sensitive to her with half a Soul? she who from all aspects is so intimately One, One divine indivisible life? Believe me it is a childish experiment, to wish to see this being without love. You look at me as though you do not know me? Indeed I have become strange to myself these last days, since her being has been so living in me.

O why cannot I give her to you? I cried.

Desist! he said. Do not comfort me, for here is nothing to comfort. I am lonely, lonely and like an hourglass, my life runs out.

Great soul! I cried, must it then come to that with you?

Be content! he said. I already began to wilt, when we found

each other in Smyrna. Forsooth! when I was still a cabin boy and my spirit and all limbs became strong and quick with raw diet, in courageous work! When then in the clear air after a stormy night I hung there at the top of the mast, beneath the fluttering flag, and looked out over the shining deeps to the sea birds, when often in battle our angry ships rooted up the sea like a boar's tooth the Earth and I stood at my captain's side with a bright mien — then I lived, O then I lived! And long after, when then the young Tenosian met me on the shores of Smyrna, with his earnestness, his love, and my hardened soul was once again thawed by the glances of the youth and learnt to love and held everything holy that is too good to be mastered, when I began with him a new life, and new powers, more full of Soul, germinated in me to a delight in the world, and to a struggle with it, then I hoped again — ah! and everything that I hoped and had was connected with you; I seized hold of you, wanted to draw you into my fate with force, lost you, found you again, our friendship only was my world, my honour, my fame; now that also is finished for ever and all my existence is in vain.

Is it then true? I replied with a sigh.

True as the Sun, he cried, but let it be! everything is taken care of.

How is that, my Alabanda? I said.

Let me tell you, he said. I have never fully spoken to you of a certain thing. And then — then it also calms both you and me a little if we speak of what is past. I once walked helplessly along the harbour of Trieste. The pirate ship on which I served, had been wrecked a few years previously, and I had barely saved myself together with a few others, on the shores of Seville. My captain was drowned, and my life and my streaming clothes was all that remained to me. I undressed and rested in the sunshine and dried the clothes on the bushes. Thereupon I went further on the road to the town. Still before the gates, I saw gay company in the gardens, went in, and sang a merry Greek song. A sad one I knew not. I was burning at the same time with shame and pain, to thus display my misfortune. I was an eighteen year old boy, wild and proud, and hated like death to become an object for men. Forgive me, I said, when I had finished my song; I have just come from the shipwreck and for today do not know what better service to give the world than to sing to you. I had said that, as far as it went, in the Spanish language. A man with a distinguished face came up to me, gave me money and with a smile said in our language: There! buy yourself a grindstone with it and learn knife-grinding and wander thus through dry land. The advice pleased me. Sir! indeed I will, I replied. I was, in addition, richly bestowed by the others and went and did as the man had advised me, and thus for a while roved about Spain and France.

What I experienced in this time, how the thousandfold forms of servitude sharpened my love of freedom and how, out of much severe want, my fortitude and cleverness grew, I have often told you with pleasure.

I pursued my wandering guiltless daily work with delight, yet finally it became soured for me.

It was taken for disguise, because I did not care at the same time to appear too vulgar, it was imagined, that I secretly conducted a dangerous business, and I was actually put into prison twice. That moved me then to give it up and with the little money I had gained,

I set out on my return to the home, from which I had once run away. I was already in Trieste and wanted to go down through Dalmatia. Then I fell ill from the difficult journey and my little wealth was consumed by that. So, half-recovered, I sadly went to the port of Trieste. All at once the man who had once assisted me on the shores of Seville, stood before me. He was strangely pleased to see me again, told me that he had often thought of me, and asked me how it had gone with me in the meantime. I told him all. I see, he cried, that it was not in vain to send you for a while into the school of Fate. You have learnt patience, you should now act, if you will.

His speech, his tone, the pressure of his hand, his mien, his look, that all, like the power of a God, all affected my being, that through much suffering was now much more inflammable than before, and I surrendered.

The man, Hyperion, of whom I speak, was one of those with whom you saw me in Smyrna. He introduced me immediately on the following night into a solemn company. A feeling of awe overcame me as I went into the Hall and, as I entered, my companion indicated the serious men and said: This is the League of Nemesis. Intoxicated by the great active sphere that opened before me I solemnly committed my blood and my soul to these men. Soon afterwards the assembly was dissolved, in order to be renewed in a few years elsewhere and each set out on the directed path, that he had to take through the world. I was joined to those with whom you found me a few years later in Smyrna.

The constraint under which I lived tormented me often, also I saw little of the great operations of the League and my desire for action found poor nourishment. However none of this sufficed to induce me to a revolt. The passion for you finally seduced me. I have said to you often enough, I was as though without Air and Sun, when you were gone; and I had no other choice; I had to give up you or my League. What I chose, you see.

But all action of man has at the end its punishment and only the Gods and the children are untouched by Nemesis.

I preferred the divine right of the heart. For the sake of my favourite, I broke my oath. Was that not fair? must not the noblest longing be the freest? — My heart had taken me at my word; I gave it freedom and you see, it needs it.

Once swear allegiance to the Genius and he pays no more heed to mortal hindrance and from you tears all bonds of life asunder.

Commitment I broke for the sake of the friend, friendship I would break for the sake of love. For Diotima's sake I would deceive you and finally murder myself and Diotima, because, for all that, we were not one. But it shall not take its course; if I must atone, for what I did, then I will do it freely; my own judge I choose for myself; those whom I failed shall have me.

Do you speak of the brothers of your League? I cried; O my Alabanda! do not do it!

What can they take from me other than my blood? he replied. Then he took me gently by the hand. Hyperion! he cried, my time is finished, and what remains to me is only a noble end. Allow me! do not belittle me and hold belief in what I say! I know as well as you, I could feign an existence for myself, could, because life's feast is consumed, still play with the crumbs, but that is not my way; not yours either. Do I need to say more? Do I not speak to you from your own soul? I thirst for Air, for freshness, Hyperion! My soul overflows of its own volition and does not stay in the old sphere any more. Soon, indeed, come the beautiful Winter days, where the dark Earth is nothing more than the foil to the shining Heavens, then it would be a good time, then, moreover, the Islands of Light shine more hospitably! — you wonder at the words? Dearest, all departing ones speak like intoxicated people, and like to act festively. When the tree begins to wither, do not all its leaves bear the colour of dawn?

Great soul, I cried, must I bear compassion for you?

I felt in his intensity how deeply he suffered. I had never experienced such woe. And yet, O Bellarmin! yet I felt the greatness of all joy, to have such a beautiful man in my eyes and arms. Yes! go and die, I cried, die! Your heart is glorious enough, your life is ripe, like the grapes on an Autumn day. Go, perfect one! I would go with you, if there were no Diotima.

Do I have you then? replied Alabanda, do you speak thus? how deep, how full of soul is everything when once my Hyperion grasps it. He flatters, I cried, to entice from me the indiscreet words for a second time! good Gods! to gain permission from me for the journey to the criminal court and death sentence!

I do not flatter, he replied earnestly, I have a right to do what you would hinder, and no common one! honour that!

There was a fire in his eyes, that, like a command of the Gods, struck me down and I was ashamed to say even a word more against him.

They will not, I thought meanwhile, they cannot do it. It is too meaningless, to slaughter such a glorious life like a sacrificial animal, and this belief calmed me.

It was a strange prize, to hear him speak again, the following night, after each one had prepared for his own journey and, before daybreak, had gone out again to be once more alone together.

Do you know, he said, among other things, why I have never scorned death? I feel within myself a life, that no God created, and no mortal begot. I believe, that we exist through ourselves, and only out of free desire are so deeply bounden with the All.

Such a thing I have never heard from you, I replied.

Also what were, he continued, what were this world, if it were not a harmony of free beings? if, from the beginning, the living, out of their own joyful drive did not work together in it in one full-voiced life, how wooden it would be, how cold? what a heartless clumsy piece of work it would be?

So here it would be in the highest sense true, I replied, that without freedom all is dead.

Yes indeed, he cried, indeed a blade of grass would not grow, if an individual germ of life were not in it! how much more in me! and therefore, dear, because I feel free in the highest sense, because I feel myself without beginning, I therefore believe that I am without end, that I am indestructible. If a potter's hand made me, then let him smash the vessel, as it pleases him. But what lives there, must be uncreated, must be divine Nature in its core, sublime beyond all might, and all art, and therefore inviolable, eternal.

Each has his mysteries, dear Hyperion! his more secret thoughts; these were mine; since I thought.

What lives, is indestructible, remains, in its deepest servile form, free, remains One, and if you divide it even to its base, remains unhurt, and if you smash it to the quick, its Essence flies triumphantly from beneath your hands. — But the morning wind stirs; our ships are awake. O my Hyperion! I have overcome it, I have been able to pronounce the judgement of death upon my heart and to separate you and me, favourite of my life! consider me now, spare me the parting! let us be quick! come! —

A chill flew through all my limbs as he thus began.

For the sake of your faithfulness, Alabanda! I cried throwing myself down before him, must it, must it then be? You bewildered me dishonestly, you transported me into frenzy. Brother! you left me not enough time to think, to actually ask whither you are going?

I may not name the place, dear heart! he replied; we will however perhaps meet again.

Meet again? I replied; then I am one belief the richer! and so will I become richer and richer in belief and finally all will be belief in me.

Dear! let us be silent, where words do not help! let us conclude manfully! you spoil the last moments for yourself.

We had thus come closer to the harbour.

One more thing! he said, when we were at his ship. Greet your Diotima! Love one another! be happy, beautiful souls!

O my Alabanda! I cried, why cannot I go in your place?

Your calling is more beautiful, he replied; remember it! you belong to her, that lovely being is from now on your world — ah! because no happiness is without sacrifice, take me as sacrifice, O Fate, and leave the lovers in their peace! —

His heart began to overcome him, and he tore himself away from me and leapt onto the ship to shorten the parting for himself and me. I felt this moment like a thunderbolt which is followed by night and deathly stillness, but in the midst of this annihilation my soul pulled itself together, to hold him, the dear departing one, and, of their own accord, my arms flew towards him! Woe! Alabanda! Alabanda! I cried, and I heard a muffled fare well across from the ship.

HYPERION TO ALABANDA

By chance the vessel that was to bring me to Calaurea, was delayed until the evening following the morning when Alabanda was already on his way.

I remained on shore, gazed quietly into the Sea from one hour to the next, tired with the pain of departure. My spirit counted over the suffering days of slowly dying youth, and wandering, like the beautiful dove, it hovered over the future. I wanted to fortify myself, I took out my long-forgotten lute to sing myself a Song of Fate, that I once in happy, ignorant youth I had repeated after my Adamas.

You wander above in the light
On tender ground, blessed Genii!
Shining airs of the Gods
Touch you lightly
Like the artist's fingers
Sacred strings.

Fateless, like the sleeping
   Infant, breathe the Heavenly;
      Chastely protected
         In modest bud
            Blooms their spirit
               Eternally
                 And the blessèd eyes
                    Look into still
                       Eternal lucidity.

But to us it is given,
   In no place to rest,
      They vanish, they fall
         The suffering men
            Blindly from one
               Hour to the next,
                 Like water from cliff
                    To cliff thrown
                       Yearlong down into uncertainty.

Thus I sang into the strings. I had hardly finished when a boat came in, on which I immediately recognised my servant, who brought me a letter from Diotima.

So are you still on Earth? she wrote, and still see the daylight? I thought to find you elsewhere, my love! I received the letter, earlier than you afterwards wished, in which you wrote about the battle of Tschesme, and so lived for a week long in the belief that you had thrown yourself into the arms of death, before your servant arrived with the joyful news, that you were still alive. Also, apart from this, a few days after the battle, I had heard that the ship, on which I knew you to be, had gone up in flames with all men on board.

But O sweet voice! once again I heard you, was touched again, like May air, by the words of love, and your beautiful hopeful joy, the lovely phantom of our future happiness, also for a moment deceived me.

Dear dreamer, why must I wake you? why can I not say, come, and make true the beautiful days, that you promise me! But it is too late, Hyperion, it is too late. Your maiden has faded since you were gone, a fire in me has gradually consumed me, and only a little remnant remains. Be not shocked! All that is natural refines itself, and everywhere the blossom of life winds itself freer and freer of the baser matter.

Dearest Hyperion! you did not indeed, in this year, think to hear my swansong.

Continuation

Shortly after you had gone, and even in the days of departure, it began. A force in the spirit of which I was frightened, an inner life before which the life of the Earth paled and disappeared like night lamps in the dawn — shall I tell you? I would have liked to go to Delphi and build a temple to the God of Enthusiasm beneath the cliffs of ancient Parnassus, and, a new female Pythius, fire the feeble people with the words of Gods, and my soul knows, that all the god-forsaken would have opened their eyes to the virgin's mouth and their brows cleared, so powerful was the spirit of life in me! But the mortal frame became more and more tired and the grievous anxiety pulled me inexorably down. Ah! often in my quiet arbour I have wept over the roses of youth! they faded and faded, and only from tears did your maiden's cheeks appear red. They were still the former trees, it was the former bower — there once stood your Diotima, your child, Hyperion, before your happy eyes, a flower amongst the flowers and the powers of the Earth and Heaven met one another peacefully in her; now she walked, a stranger amongst the buds of May, and her intimate friends, the lovely plants, nodded to her friendlily, but she could only mourn; yet I passed none by, yet one after another I bade fare well to all the playfriends of youth, the Groves and Springs and whispering Hills.

Ah!, often with difficult sweet effort, for as long as I could, I still walked to the heights where you lived with Notara, and spoke of you with the friend, as light-heartedly as possible, so that he should not write to you about me; but soon when the heart became too loud, the dissembler stole out into the garden, and then, there I was at the parapet, above the cliffs, where once I looked down with you, and out into open Nature, ah! where I stood held by your hands, all-harkened by your eyes, in the first thrilling warming of love, and wished to pour my overflowing soul, like a sacrificial wine, out into the depths of life, then I swayed round and complained to the wind of my pain, and, like a shy bird, my glance erred and hardly dared look at the beautiful Earth from which I should part.

Continuation

Thus it has gone with your maiden, Hyperion. Ask not how? do not explain this death to yourself! He who seeks to fathom such a Fate, finally curses himself and everything, and yet no soul is guilty of it.

Shall I say the grief over you has killed me? O no! O no! indeed this was welcome to me, this grief, it gave the death, which I carried in me, form and grace; to honour your darling you are dying, I could now say to myself. —

Or has my soul become too mature for me in all the enthusiasm of our love and does she therefore now not keep me, like a high-spirited youth, in the modest home any longer? speak! was it my heart's plenty, that parted me from mortal life? has the Nature in me, through you, you glorious one! become too proud, to put up any longer with this mediocre star? But if you have taught her to fly, why do you not also teach my soul, to return to you? If you have lit the Aether-loving fire, why do you not tend it for me? — Hear me, dear! for the sake of your soul! do not accuse yourself of my death.

Could you then have stopped me, when your fate directed you the same way? and had you, in the heroic struggle of your heart, preached to me — be content, child! accommodate yourself to the times — would you not have been the most vain of all vain?

Continuation

I will tell you honestly what I think. Your fire lived in me, your spirit had passed over into me; but that would hardly have hurt, and only your fate has made my new life fatal. My Soul was too powerful for me through you, she would also have become quiet again through you. You withdrew my life from the Earth, you would have also had power to tie me to the Earth, you could have conjured me into your embracing arms like a magic circle; ah! one of your heart-felt glances would have held me fast, one of your love-declarations would again have made me into a happy healthy child; but as your own Fate drove you into spiritual loneliness, like flood waters onto a mountain peak, O only then, when I finally believed the storm of the battle had burst open the prison and my Hyperion had flown up into the ancient freedom, then with me it was decided and will soon come to an end.

I have made many words, and yet silently died the great Roman woman when in mortal combat, her Brutus and the native land fought. But what could I do better in the best of my last days of life? – Also I am ever driven to say various things. Quiet was my life; my death is eloquent. Enough!

Continuation

Just one thing I must still say to you. You would have gone down, you would have to despair, nevertheless the spirit will rescue you. You no laurel will comfort and no myrtle-wreath; Olympus will, the living, present, that, eternally young, blossoms around all your senses. The beautiful world is my Olympus; in this you will live, and with the holy beings of the world, with the Gods of Nature, with these you will be joyful.

O be welcome, you Good, you True, you greatly missed,

unrecognised! children and elders! Sun and Earth and Aether with all living souls, that play around you, around whom you play in eternal love! O take the all-endeavouring men, take the deserters again into the family of Gods, receive them into the home of Nature, from which they absconded! —

You know this invocation, Hyperion, You began it in me. You will fulfil it in yourself, and only then rest.

I have enough thereby, joyfully as a Greek maiden to die.

The poor, who know nothing, other than their needy rough work, who only serve necessity and scorn genius, and do not honour you, childlike life of Nature, they may stand in fear of death. Their yoke has become their world; Better, than their servitude, they do not know; shy away from the freedom of the Gods, that death gives us?

But not I! I have lifted myself above the imperfect works, that men's hands have made, I have felt the life of Nature that is higher than any thoughts — were I to become a plant, would that be so great a pity? — I will be. How could I lose myself out of the sphere of life, in which the Eternal Love, that is common to all, holds all natures together? how could I depart from the covenant, that binds all beings together? That does not break so easily, like the loose bonds of these times. It is not like a market day when the folk congregate and are noisy and disperse. No! by the spirit that unites us, by the divine spirit that is individual to each and common to all! no! no! in the Covenant of Nature fidelity is no dream. We part only, to be more intimately one, more divinely peaceful with all, with ourselves. We die to live.

I will be; I ask not what I will be. To be, to live, that is enough, that is the honour of the Gods; and therefore all that lives in the divine world is equal, and in it there are not masters and menials. The natures live amongst one another like lovers; all is common to them, Spirit, joy and eternal youth.

Constancy have the stars chosen, in quiet fullness of life they move continually like waves and know not age. In variation, we represent completion; in changing melodies we participate in the great accords of joy. Like harpists around the throne of the elders, we live, ourselves divine, around the quiet Gods of the world, with the fleeting song of life we soften the blessed severity of the Sun God and the others.

Look up into the world! Is she not like a wandering triumphal procession, where Nature continually celebrates her victory over all corruption? and does not life lead death with it into glory, in golden chains, as once the general led the captured kings with him? and we, we are like the virgins and youths who, with dance and song, in changing forms and tones, accompany the majestic procession.

Now let me be silent. To say more would be too much. We will meet with each other again. —

Mourning youth! soon, soon you will be happier. Your laurel has not flowered for you and your myrtle faded, for you shall be a priest of divine Nature, and the poetic days are already beginning for you.

O could I see you in your coming beauty! Fare well!

At the same time I received a letter from Notara in which he wrote to me:

The day after she had written to you for the last time, she

became quite calm, still spoke a few words, also said then, that she would prefer to depart from the Earth in fire, than to be buried, and her ashes we should gather into an urn, and put in the woods, in the place where you, my dear! had first met her. Soon after, as it became dark, she said good night to us, as though she wanted to sleep, and buried her beautiful head in her arms; until toward morning we heard her breathe. As it then became completely still and I heard nothing more, I went over to her and harkened.

O Hyperion, what further can I say? It was finished and our laments wakened her no more.

It is a terrible mystery, that such a life should die and I will admit to you, I myself have neither sense or belief, since I witnessed it.

Yet better always is a beautiful death, Hyperion, than such an indolent life as ours now is.

To ward off the flies, that is henceforth our work and to gnaw on the things of the world, like children the fig root, that finally is our joy. To become old amongst youthful people seems to me a pleasure, but to become old, there where everything is old, seems to me worse than anything. —

I would almost like to advise you, my Hyperion! that you do not come here. I know you. It would rob you of your senses. Apart from that you are not safe here. My dear! think of Diotima's mother, think of me and spare yourself!

I must admit to you, I shudder when I consider your fate. But yet I also think, that the burning Summer does not dry up the deeper springs, only the shallow rain streams. I have seen you in moments, Hyperion! where you seemed to me to be a higher being.

You are now put to the test and it is bound to become clear who you are. Fare well.

Thus wrote Notara; and you ask, my Bellarmin! how I am now whilst I relate this to you?

Best one! I am calm, for I wish for nothing better, than the Gods. Must not everything suffer? And the more excellent it is, the more profound! Does not holy Nature suffer? O my Divinity! that you can mourn when you are blissful, that I have long not understood. But the bliss that does not suffer, is sleep, and without death there is no life. Should you continually be like a child and sleep, like the nothingness? do without the victory? not run through all the perfections? Yes! yes! pain is worthy of lying on the heart of man, and to be your intimate, O Nature! For he alone leads from one bliss to another, and there is no other companion than he. —

At that time, as I again began to revive, I wrote to Notara from Sicily, whither a ship from Paros had at first brought me:

I have obeyed you, my dear! am already far from you and will now also give news; but words will be difficult for me; that I may as well admit. The Blessèd, where Diotima now is, do not speak much; in my night, in the depths of the mourning one, is speech also at an end.

A beautiful death has my Diotima died; you are right; it is also that which awakens me and gives me my soul again.

But it is the former world no more, to which I return. I am a stranger, like the unburied, when they come up from Acheron, and were I on my native island, in the gardens of my youth, that my father closed to me, ah! even then, even then, would I be a stranger on Earth and no God would connect me any more with the past.

Yes! all is past. That I must just keep saying to myself, must thereby bind my Soul, so that she remains calm, does not excite herself with absurd childish attempts.

All is past and could I even now weep, beautiful Divinity, as you once wept for Adonis, even then my Diotima would not return to me and my heart's word has lost its strength, for only the breezes hear me.

O God! and that I am myself nothing, and the meanest manual worker can say, he has done more than I! that they can comfort themselves, the poor in spirit, and smile and scold me as a dreamer, because my deeds did not come to fruition, because my arms are not free, because my times are like the raging Procrustes, who threw the men, that he caught, into a child's cradle, and so that they fitted in the little bed, hacked off their limbs.

Would it not be all too desperate to throw oneself amongst the foolish masses and become torn apart by them! or should a noble blood just not be ashamed, to mix itself with the blood of knaves! O if only there were a banner, Gods! under which my Alabanda might serve, a Thermopylæ, where, with honour I could shed the blood, all the lonely love that will never be of use to me. Still better it would be, truly, if I could live, live, in the new temples in the newly assembled Agora of our people, with great joy, calm the great grief; but of that I will not speak, for I will weep away my strength entirely if I think of it all.

Ah Notara! also with me it is finished; spoilt for me is my own Soul, because I must reproach her, that Diotima is dead, and the thoughts of my youth, that I greatly respected, are valid for me no more. Indeed have they not poisoned my Diotima for me!

And now tell me where is there still a refuge? — Yesterday I was up on Aetna. There the great Sicilian came to mind, who once, tired of counting the hours, intimate with the Soul of the World, in his bold love of life threw himself into the glorious flames; for the cold poet must have had to warm himself at the fire, said a mocker afterwards.

O how gladly I would have drawn such mockery upon myself! but one must respect oneself more than I respect myself, so uncalled to fly into the heart of Nature, or as you otherwise like to call it, for really! as I now am, I have no names for things and everything is uncertain to me.

Notara! and now tell me where is there still refuge?

In the woods of Calauria? — Yes! there in the green darkness, where our trees, the confidants of our love, where, like an evening glow, their dying leaves fall onto Diotima's urn and their beautiful heads bow over Diotima's urn, gradually ageing, until they also sink down over the belovèd ashes, — there, there I could well live as I wanted!

But you would advise me to stay away, think, I would not be safe in Calaurea and that could well be.

I know well, you will refer me to Alabanda. But only listen! he is crushed! weather-beaten is the strong, slender trunk, also he, and the young boys will pick up the splinters and make a merry fire with them. He is gone; he has certain good friends, who will relieve him, who are really very skilled, in helping out every one on whom life imposes somewhat heavily; these he has gone to visit, and why? because there is nothing other for him to do, or if you would know all, because a passion gnaws at his heart, and do you also know for whom? for Diotima, whom he still believes to be alive, married to me and happy — poor Alabanda! now she belongs to you and to me!

He travelled out to the East and I, I take a ship to the North West, because that is how opportunity will have it. —

And now fare well, all of you! all you dear ones, you whom I have had at heart, friends of my youth and you parents and you dear Greeks all, you suffering ones!

You breezes, you that nourished me in tender childhood, and you dark laurel woods and you coastal cliffs and you majestic waters, you who taught my Spirit to sense what is great — and ah! you images of mourning, you where my melancholy began, holy walls with which the heroic cities girded themselves, and you ancient gates, through which many a beautiful wanderer passed, you temple pillars and you ruins of the Gods! and you, O Diotima! and you valleys of my love, and you streams, you who once saw the holy figure, you trees, where she was happy, you Springtimes, where she lived, the gracious one, with the flowers, depart, depart not from me! but if it shall be, you sweet remembrances! then you also are extinguished and leave me, for man can alter nothing and the light of life comes and departs as it will.

HYPERION TO BELLARMIN

So I came amongst the Germans. I asked but little and was resigned to find yet less. Humbly I came, like the homeless blind Oedipus to the gate of Athens, where the Grove of the Gods received him; and beautiful souls came to meet him —

How other it went with me!

Barbarians since antiquity, through diligence and science and through religion itself grown more barbaric, profoundly incapable of every divine feeling, ruined to the core to take pleasure in the holy Graces, in every degree of excess and meanness offensive to every good-natured soul, dull and inharmonious, like the fragments of a discarded vessel — those, my Bellarmin! were my comforters.

It is a harsh thing to say and yet I say it, because it is true: I can think of no people more torn than the Germans. Artisans you see, but no human beings, thinkers, but no human beings, priests, but no human beings, masters and servants, youths and mature people, but no human beings — is that not like a battlefield, where hands and arms and all limbs lie dismembered amongst one another, whilst the shed life-blood runs away into the sand?

Each one pursues his own, you will say, and I say it also. Only that he must pursue it with his whole soul, must not stifle each power within himself, if it does not exactly fit in with his title, must not with this niggardly anxiety, literally only dissemble that which he is called, with seriousness, with love he must be what he is, then lives a spirit in what he does, and if he is forced into a branch of work, where the spirit is not permitted to live at all, then let him thrust it away with scorn and learn to plough! Your Germans, however, like to stay with what is most expedient, and therefore they produce so much indifferent and so little free and truly pleasing work. Yet that could be suffered, if only such people were not insensitive to all beautiful life, if only everywhere there were not the curse of godforsaken unnaturalness on such folk. —

The virtues of the ancients are merely brilliant mistakes, once said, I know not what malicious tongue; and yet however, their mistakes themselves are virtues, for then there still lived a childlike, a beautiful spirit, and in all they did nothing was done without soul. The virtues of the Germans however are a brilliant evil and nothing more; for they are only works of necessity, through cowardly anxiety, rung out of the barren heart with slavish effort, and leave desolate every pure soul who would gladly gain sustenance from the Beautiful, ah! who spoilt by the divine harmony in more noble natures cannot bear the discord which is screaming in all the dead regulation of these people.

I say to you: there is nothing holy, that is not desecrated, not degraded into a mean expedient by these people, and what even amongst savages mainly keeps itself divinely pure, this too these all-calculating barbarians pursue, in the same way as one pursues a trade, and cannot do otherwise, for where once a human being is broken in, then it serves its end, then it is useful, it is no more enthusiastic, God forbid! it stays fixed, and when it celebrates and when it loves and when its prays and even, when the Spring's lovely festival, when the reconciling time of the world dissolves all sorrows, and innocence works magic in a guilty heart, when drunk from the Sun's warm beam, the slave joyfully forgets his chains, and when, calmed by the divinely-souled Air, the misanthropists are peaceable, like the children — when even the caterpillar takes on wings and the bee swarms, the German still stays in his compartment and does not bother much about the weather!

But you will judge, holy Nature! For, if only they were modest, these people, did not make themselves into laws for the better people amongst them! if only they did not revile, what they are not, and if, however, they want to revile, if only they did not mock the Divine! —

Or is it not divine, that which you mock and call soulless? Is not the Air that you drink better than your idle talk? the Sun's beams, are they not more precious, than all you wise ones? the Earth's springs and the morning dew refreshes your grove; can you also do that? ah! kill, you can, but not bring to life, if Love does not do it, which is not from you, which you did not invent. You worry and plan to escape Fate and do not understand when your childish tricks do not help; meanwhile harmlessly above wander the stars. You debase, you tear apart patient Nature, where she suffers you, yet she lives on, in infinite youth, and her Autumn and her Spring you cannot drive away, her Aether, that you destroy not.

Oh divine she must be, because you may destroy her, and still she does not age and despite you, the Beautiful remains beautiful! —

It is also heart-breaking, when one sees your poets, your artists, and, all who still respect Genius, who love the Beautiful and care for it. The good ones! They live in the world like strangers in their own house, they are just like the patient Ulysses, when in the form of a beggar, he sat at his doors, whilst the brazen suitors made uproar in the hall and asked, who has brought us this tramp?

Full of love and spirit and hope their sons of the Muse grow up amongst the German people; you see them seven years later, and they wander, like the shades, silent and cold, are like a ground, that the enemy has sown with salt, that it may never produce a grass-stalk; and when they speak, woe to he! who understands them, who but sees in the furious titanic strength, as in their protean arts a battle of despair, which their deranged beautiful spirit is fighting with the barbarians, with whom it has to deal.

Everything on Earth is imperfect, is the old saw of the Germans. If only someone would say to one of these godforsaken, that everything is so imperfect with them, because they will not let anything pure be unspoilt, not let anything holy be untouched by their coarse hands, that nothing flourishes with them, because they do not respect the root of growth, divine Nature, that really their life is shallow and full of care and too full of cold dumb dissension, because they despise the Genius, which brings strength and nobility into human action, and serenity into suffering and love and brotherhood into towns and houses.

And therefore they fear death so much, for the sake of an oyster-like life, suffer all humiliations, because they know nothing higher, than their rough work that they have cobbled together for themselves.

O Bellarmin! where a folk loves the Beautiful, where it respects the Genius in its artists, there moves, like life-sustaining Air, an all-pervading spirit, there the shy mind opens up, the darkness of self-conceit melts away, and innocent and great are all hearts, and Enthusiasm brings forth heroes. The home of all men is with such a people and gladly the stranger likes to linger. But where divine Nature and her artists are so insulted, ah! then the best delight of life is gone, and every other star is better than the Earth. More barren, more desolate become the people, who yet are all born beautiful; the servile spirit grows, with it the uncouth mind, drunkenness increases with cares, and with sensuality, hunger and the cares of life; the blessing of each year becomes a curse and all Gods flee.

And woe the stranger who out of love, journeys and would come to such a people, and threefold woe to he, who as I, driven by great grief, a beggar of my kind, comes to such people! –

Enough! you know me, will take it in good part, Bellarmin! I spoke in your name also, I spoke for all who are in this land, and suffer as I there suffered.

HYPERION TO BELLARMIN

I now wanted to leave Germany again. I sought nothing more amongst this race, I was enough offended, by pitiless insults, did not want my soul to completely bleed to death amongst such people.

But the heavenly Spring arrested me; it was the sole joy that remained to me, indeed it was my last love, moreover how could I think of other things and also leave the country where it was?

Bellarmin! I had never so fully experienced that old constant word of Fate, that a new bliss opens up for the heart, if it perseveres and endures the midnight of affliction, and that, like the song of the nightingale in the dark, the Song of Life that the world sings to us, first sounds divine in profound grief. For, as though with Genii, I lived now with the blossoming trees, and the clear brooks, that flowed beneath, whispered, like the voices of Gods, the sorrow from my bosom. And thus it happened to me everywhere, you loved one! — when I rested in the grass, and delicate life was green about me, when I walked up the warm hill, where the wild rose grew about the stony path, also when I took a ship round the breezy banks of the great river and all the islands that it tenderly nurses.

And when often in the mornings, like the invalid to the

medicinal waters, I climbed through the sleeping flowers to the peak of the mountain but near me the dear birds, satisfied with sweet sleep, flew from the bushes, whirling in the twilight and eager for the day, and already the livelier Air now carried up the prayers of the valleys, the voices of flocks and the sounds of the morning bell, and now the sublime light, the divinely-bright, came down the usual path, conjuring the Earth with immortal life, so that her heart warmed and all her children came to life again — O, like the moon, that still remained in the sky, to share the joys of the day, so I also stood the lonely one, above the plains, and wept tears of love to the shores below and the gleaming waters, and long could not take my eyes away.

Or in the evenings, when far into the valley I came upon the cradle of the Spring where the dark heights of the oaks rustled all around, me, like a sacred dying one, Nature buried in her peace when the Earth then was a shadow and imperceptible life whispered through the branches, through the peaks and above the peaks stood the evening cloud, a gleaming mountain from where Heaven's beams flowed towards me like streams, to give drink to the thirsty wanderer —

O Sun, O you Airs, I cried then, with you alone my heart still lives, as amongst brothers!

Thus, more and more, I gave myself to blessèd Nature and almost too boundlessly. I would indeed so gladly have become as a child, to be nearer her, would indeed have so gladly known less and would have become like the pure ray of light to be nearer to her! O one moment in her peace, to feel her beauty, how much more that is worth to me, than years full of thought, than all endeavours of all-endeavouring men! Like ice, what I had learnt, what I had done in life melted, and all projects of youth died away in me; and O you dear ones, you who are far, you dead and you living, how ardently One we were!

Once I sat far in a field, by a fountain, in the shadow of ivy-green cliffs and overhanging blossoming bushes. It was the most beautiful midday I had known. Sweet airs blew and in the morning freshness the land still gleamed and, quiet in its homely Aether, the light smiled. The men had gone to their domestic boards to rest from work; alone was my love with the Spring, and an inexplicable yearning was in me. Diotima, I cried, where are you, O where are you? And it was to me as though I heard Diotima's voice, the voice that once delighted me in the days of joy —

With my own, she cried, am I, with yours, that the erring spirit of men does not recognise!

A tender shock lay hold of me and my thoughts died gently away in me.

O dear words from a holy mouth, I cried, when I awoke again, dear enigma, do I comprehend you?

And once for all I looked back again into the cold night of men and shuddered and wept for joy, that I was so blessed and spoke words, so it seemed to me, but they were like the fire's roar, when it flares up and leaves behind it the ashes —

"O you, so I thought, with your Gods, Nature! I have dreamt away the dream of the things of humanity, and say, only you live, and what the unpeaceful ones forced, fabricated, like pearls of wax, melts away in your flames!

How long is it that they have dispensed with you? O how long is it that their masses have reviled you, profanely named you and your Gods, the Living, the Blessedly Peaceable!

Men fall like rotten fruit from you, O let them perish, that they return to your roots again, and I, O Tree of Life, that I become green again with you and breathe around your crown with all your budding branches! peaceful and intimate, for we all grow from the golden grain of seed upwards!

You Springs of the Earth! you Flowers! and you Woods and you Eagles and you brotherly Light! how old and new is our love! — Free we are, resemble each other, not anxiously from without; why should the manner of life not vary? for we all love the Aether and in our innermost being resemble each other.

Also we, also we are not parted, Diotima, and the tears for you do not understand it. Living tones we are, tuned together in your harmony, Nature! who rends them? who may part lovers? –

O Soul! Soul! Beauty of the World! you Imperishable! you Rapturous! with your eternal youth! You Are; what then is death and all the woe of men? — Ah! much have the wayward made of empty words. Yet all comes to pass through fancy, and yet all ends with peace.

Like the quarrels of lovers, are the dissonances of the world. Reconciliation is in the midst of strife and all that is parted finds itself again.

The arteries divide and return to the heart and one, eternal glowing life is All."

Thus I thought. More shortly.

Friedrich Hölderlin — Lightning Conductor of the Divine

INDIA RUSSELL

Published in *Temenos Academy Review* 2008, the following article is a version of a lecture presented to the Temenos Academy on 14th November 2007 and reproduced here with kind permission of the editor. I include this to show the parallel between the lives of Hölderlin and his character, Hyperion.

    I.R.

All translations from German are my own.

Friedrich Hölderlin — Lightning Conductor of the Divine
INDIA RUSSELL

Es wird nur Eine Schönheit seyn; und Menschheit und Natur wird sich vereinen in Eine allumfassende Gottheit.[1]

INTRODUCTION
A brief consideration of Hölderlin, Shelley and Empedocles as fellow visionaries and proclaimers of Divine Nature.

My seemingly dramatic title, which was based on my innate feeling for Hölderlin's poetry and on my own experience as a poet, was further endorsed when I recently read *Dichterberuf* (Vocation of the Poet), in which Hölderlin writes of the phenomenon of poets being shot through by a bolt or flash of the creative Divine so that their very being shakes; of their being, in fact, a lightning conductor of the Divine:

> Und dennoch, o ihr Himmlischen all, und all
> > Ihr Quellen und ihr Ufer und Hain' und Höhn,
> > > Wo wunderbar zuerst, als du die
> > > > Loken ergriffen, und unvergeßlich

> Der unverhoffte Genius über uns
> > Der schöpferische, göttliche kam, daß stumm
> > > Der Sinn uns ward und, wie vom
> > > > Strale gerührt, das Gebein erbebte . ...

And yet O you Divine Ones all, and all
    You Springs and you Banks and Groves and Mountains
        Where wonderful at first as you
            Seized our locks, and unforgettably

The unexpected Genius over us
    The creative, divine, came, so that the
        Mind became silent to us and, as struck
            By lightning, our frames shook ...

This is completely understandable and I feel is an experience shared by Shelley and Empedocles. Divine Nature, which I shall refer to often, is to be understood as described in the above excerpt and obviously not as a beautiful backdrop to the life of superior Man, to be objectively admired (or not) or written about in what is termed 'nature poetry'. Nature, in the sense in which Hölderlin uses the term, is the Divine force emanating from the sky and the sea, the trees and the birds and animals. She is a powerful mystery who reveals herself to seers who, as Hölderlin writes, remain *wachend bei Nacht* 'watching by night'. If I were asked for a few words to describe Hölderlin's work I would say piety, beauty, rhythm, vision, truth and oneness with Nature.

The powerful beauty of the German language was awoken in me, when I was young, by Bach's *Matthäuspassion*. For many years I spent every Good Friday at the Festival Hall immersed in that profoundly moving work and can still hear the Evangelist, his voice at one with the music and the sublime language of the Lutheran Bible. I enrolled for an intensive course at the Goethe Institut in Exhibition Road and then went to Nürnberg and taught in a Steiner Schule and was soon practising Eurythmy to the solemnly intoned words *'Alle Gestalten sind ähnlich, und keine gleichet der andern'* of Goethe's *Die Metamrphose der Pflanzen.*[2] On being accepted at University College London, having given 'the beauty of the language' as my reason for wanting to study German, I discovered to my amazed delight the eighteenth-century poet, Friedrich Hölderlin. Until then I had only vaguely heard of him; but he came to me now as a close friend who had always been there, but just hidden in the shadows, and with what joyful recognition!

One of the first English books to be published on the poet was Ronald Peacock's *Hölderlin*, which opens with the declaration,

Amongst German poets Hölderlin is the one whose name can be uttered only in the tone of veneration, for in none was there to such a degree radiant purity.

He continues,

… his work is inseparable from himself in a quite unusual measure. It is unsullied, immaculate.

And concludes,

He is innocent, like the nature to which his first reverence is paid.[3]

A copy of the Methuen reprint of his book, issued after an interval of nearly forty years, was given to me by Professor Peacock when, liking my ideas and my enthusiasm for Hölderlin, he offered me my first job on the academic ladder, as he called it, teaching Science-German in his Department at Bedford College. The inscription reads – 'With best wishes for your Hölderlin project'. It is still in progress!

My first volumes of Hölderlin's work are covered with neat pencilled exclamation marks, squiggles and exclamations: *Yes! Yes!,* *c.f. my dream/poem etc.* It was the delicate simplicity of his language embodying Truth I found so recognizable, as in these few lines from *Der Tod des Empedokles* (The Death of Empedokles, II iv):[4]

> *Es kommt und geht die Freunde, doch gehört*
> *Sie Sterblichen nicht eigen, und der Geist*
> *Eilt ungefragt auf seinem Pfade weiter.*
> *Ach! können wir denn sagen, daß du da*
> *Gewesen?*

> It comes and goes, Joy, but
> Does not belong to mortals, and the Spirit
> Hastens on, unquestioned, on its path.
> Oh! can we say then, that you were
> Ever there?

And it was his epistolary novel *Hyperion* that entranced me – and I use 'entranced' in its original meaning. His language is like a magic spell. He seems to tune into the language of the trees and the wind, the stars and the sky, which were to him living deities, bringing their timeless rhythms into his poetry. He breaks the bonds of Time with his other-worldly music. It is not surprising that he became fascinated by the figure of Empedocles who, as he writes, 'tired of hour-counting', chose to re-unite himself with timeless Nature, who had revealed herself to him in all her unified and wondrous beauty, by casting himself into Mount Etna. A strange story, yes. But when one has been in close communion with Nature and is continually jerked back into the time-bound world full of rhythm-less, unsympathetic people, when one, like the young Hyperion, is 'so laughably accompanied by the raucous shrillness of the world in [his] heart's dearest melodies'; then it is not such an odd thing to wish to reunite oneself with the sympathetic confidante one has and to attempt to cross the apparent boundary between one another. My Shelley edition has similar enthusiastic markings. He too entered into the life of Nature. His 'thinking organs' (πραπιδες), as the historical Empedocles calls those faculties that reach out beyond the known world, could enter into the being of things. Hölderlin, Shelley, Empedocles – all call for a respect for Nature for all have entered into her world and seen, like Blake, not 'a green thing that stands in the way' but a living God.

In a long letter to Howard Gaskill, now a Professor of German, I discuss some of Hölderlin's late poems and show how he is trying to bring together the timeless essence of the time-bound past – Greek and Christian – into one holy and united song of praise. In his late poem *Die Titanen* (The Titans) Hölderlin implies that it is *Gesang*, which can be understood as hymnic, harmonious unity, which frees the spirit from the prison of Time and mortality and, like the song of the birds and the humming of the bees, returns it 'Back to the burning fountain whence it came' (to quote Shelley), back to its source which is both *der Gott in uns* – the God in us – and *der Geist der Welt* – the Spirit of the World – thereby closing the circle in a continuous round of praise of creation for the Creator and the Creator for creation. And this is what, as Hölderlin says in the now famous penultimate letter of *Hyperion*, the Germans do not do. And their failure to connect with their source has brought about complete fragmentation,[5] so that Germany looks like

… ein Schlachtfeld, wo Hände und Arme und alle Glieder zerstükelt untereinanderliegen, indessen das vergoßne Lebensblut im Sande zerrinnt …

… a battlefield, where hands and arms and all the limbs lie about in pieces whilst the spilt blood runs away into the sand …[6]

For Hölderlin, men have failed, as yet, to 'help Heaven' (*helfen/Dem Himmel*), because they are too bound by Time and mortality. That the birds and the bees help Heaven is understood by Hölderlin. In *Die Titanen*, he writes,

Mich aber umsummet

Die Bien und wo der Akersmann

Die Furchen machet singen gegen

Dem Lichte die Vögel. Manche helfen

Dem Himmel. Diese siehet

Der Dichter.

But around me hums

The bee and where the ploughman

Makes his furrow the birds

Sing towards the light. Many help

Heaven. This the poet

Sees.

Die Titanen, like much of Hölderlin's late work, is considered difficult and is the subject of much scholarship. After reading the poem I dreamt the meaning of it, seeing a divine connection, the lightning of the Gods being 'harmlessly channelled through the poet, the *Blitzleiter* (*lightning conductor*), back to its source thereby closing the circle'. I still have the fading file paper with the detailed vision. When I told my supervisor about it he said it was amazing and tallied with modern scholarship; but it was not acceptable as I had not read any of the criticism and it was a dream, not scholarship!

That language distinguishes Man from the rest of the animals is a commonplace. But its corollary is not so common: it is Song that distinguishes Nature from Man – Song in the sense of a Hymn of the Universe. Hölderlin in his poetry is working towards the freeing of man from the bonds of speech, which is time-bound,

into the timeless *Gesang* of Nature, which is a Hymn of Praise for
the Divine.

*

In Eurythmy, vowels and consonants are expressed by gesture,
movement and colour. One preparatory exercise is 'the spear-
thrower' – a leaning back with a javelin, tuning into the rhythm of
the universe and gathering energy before speaking, and then sending
the words out along the flow. And this to me is what Hölderlin is
doing – tuning into original universal rhythm. In Theodor Storm's
beautiful novella *Immensee*, Reinhard and Elisabeth have just sung
the folk song *Ich stand auf hohen Bergen* and as they finish, the same
song comes floating up to them sung by a shepherd in the valley.
And Reinhard says:

> *Hört ihr es wohl? So geht's von Mund zu Mund … Das sind*
> *Urtöne; sie schlafen in Waldesgründen.*

> You hear that? Thus it passes from mouth to mouth …
> Those are original tones, they sleep in the depths of the
> forest.[7]

I have just re-read *Hyperion*. And what remains is the song or
Urtöne. It is like an elemental piece of music – an Aeolian harp
on which the Divine Spirit of Nature plays. The μουσικη of the
Greeks must have been like this:[8] not chanting, not song, but an
elemental and rhythmical music, speaking directly to the soul.[9]

In his brief introduction to *Hyperion*, a novel or prose-poem on the life of a young Greek brought up in Germany who returns to Greece with the Shelleyan desire to help another Athens to arise, Hölderlin writes,

> He who merely smells my plant, knows it not, and he who
> picks it, merely to learn from it, does not know it either.

He had to wait a hundred years for an empathetic scholar, Norbert von Hellingrath, to understand his work in the way he wished.

One must go beyond the writing in order to appreciate it – back, on the wings of the melody, back on the rhythm that has carried it to the poet, to the inspirational source that Shelley is talking about in his *Defence of Poetry* of 1821.

Hölderlin is not just a poet. He is a visionary. He gave his whole being to Nature and the, to him, living Gods; and they, like lightning searching for a conductor to connect them with the earth, pulsed through him, changing his vision and his very speech.

*

The landscape of Swabia, Hölderlin's birthplace, must in the eighteenth century have been of a harmonious beauty difficult for us to visualize even with the help of contemporary paintings and engravings. But we can get a sense of it in Hölderlin's late poem *Der Nekar* (The Neckar), dedicated to the river which flowed through all his life:

In your valleys my heart awoke to life
In me, your waves played about me,
And all the gracious hills that know you
Wanderer, none is foreign to me.

On their summits Heaven's air freed
Me often from the pains of bondage; and from the valley
Like life from the cup of joy
Glanced the blueish silver wave.

The springs of the mountains hurried down to you,
With them also my heart, and you took us with you
To the calmly noble Rhine, down to his
Towns and gay islands.

Still seems the world lovely to me, and my eye runs from me
Longingly after the charms of the earth,
To golden Pactolus, to Smyrna's
Shore, to Ilion's wood. Also often

I would like to land near Sunium, ask the silent
Path of your pillars, Olympieum!
Before tempest and age
Down into the ruins of the temples of Athens

And their statues of Gods bury you as well,
    For long now you have stood lonely, O Pride of the World
        That is no more. And O you beautiful
            Islands of Ionia where the sea's breeze

Cools the hot shores and through the laurel wood
    Rustles, when the sun warms the vine,
        Ah, where a golden Autumn changes
            The sighs of a poor folk into songs,

When his pomegranate tree ripens, when through the green night
    The orange shines, and the mastic tree
        Runs with resin, and kettle drum and cymbal
            Sound to the labyrinthian dance,

To you, you islands, perhaps to you will my
    Guardian God bring me; but even there will
        My Neckar never leave my faithful mind with his
            Lovely meadows and willows on his banks.

Nürtingen on the Neckar, where Hölderlin lived from the age of four, was an important wine-producing area – his half-brother, Karl Gock, was the local *Weingraf.* Vineyards and wheat fields, orchards and gentle meadows and hills embracing *Dörfer* and *Städtchen* surrounded Hölderlin with their beauty from birth. *Brot und Wein*, a now much discussed poem, particularly with regard to the question of whether Hölderlin was a Christian, to me reflects not just the sacrament of the Church but the natural sacrament of Mother Nature with her gifts of bread and wine. But over this Divine, gift-bringing landscape breathed a strict pietistic, messianic religion. Hölderlin's mother came from a long line of priests, as did his father, and Hölderlin was sent to the Tübinger Stift, a Protestant seminary regarded as one of the great centres of religious and classical scholarship, to prepare him for a life preaching the Word of God. He did of course do this, but not within the confines of the Lutheran church, and not the word of one God only. His church was primarily the church of *Mutter Erde* and *Vater Aether* and his Gods were all the prophets including the youngest, Christ, all of whom he saw as messengers of the Divine.

Hölderlin's divergence from his expected path has a parallel in Shelley's life. But, more interestingly, it is the poets' experience of Timelessness, and of literally going beyond themselves and becoming the Divine Vision, that links them in spirit with each other and with the poet-philosopher, Empedocles. As Jeremy Naydler points out, Plato held that:

> True knowledge is knowledge by participation. So to know the Form of the Good one must know it through a participation in its essence, a knowing that, as Plato describes it, is tantamount to a visionary and ecstatic experience.[10]

This is what Hölderlin, Shelley and Empedocles are all writing about – and this is what the majority of critics do not seem to understand, often calling the visionary experience 'symbolism' or 'metaphor'. Shelley has for a moment become the skylark, as Hölderlin became the river or wood or mountain. They see 'thro', not 'with', the eye. And they see with Love.

It is interesting to compare these two accounts of 'thinking organs':

There was among them a man of exceptional knowledge
who indeed obtained the greatest wealth in his thinking organs,
master of all kinds of particularly wise deeds;
for whenever he reached out with all his thinking organs
he easily saw each of all things which are
in ten or twenty lifetimes.[11]

And in the moonless nights, when the dun ocean
   Heaved underneath wide heaven, star-impearled,
Starting from dreams ...
   Communed with the immeasurable world;
And felt his life beyond his limbs dilated,
   Till his mind grew like that it contemplated.[12]

Empedocles, a follower of the Pythagorean School, expresses, like Shelley and Hölderlin, a deep and reverential understanding of Nature. In *On Nature* and *Purifications*, thought to be parts of one poem, he writes:

All were tame and gentle to men,
   both beasts and birds, and loving thoughts blazed on.[13]

Aristotle, in his *Rhetoric*, writes of Empedocles' teaching:

For, as everyone intuitively suspects, there exists a natural and common justice and injustice, even if there is no mutual community or agreement … and as Empedocles says on the topic of not killing animals – for this is not just for some and unjust for others:

But what is lawful for all extends continuously
through the wide-ruling aither and through the boundless gleam.[14]

This is precisely the view of Shelley, expressed in his poetry and in *A Vindication of Natural Diet*, which so shocked the sensibilities of his English readers. He is addressing, he writes, 'the ardent devotee of truth and virtue'. In *Queen Mab* we read,

Throughout this varied and eternal world
Soul is the only element: the block
That for uncounted ages has remained
The moveless pillar of a mountain's weight
Is active, living spirit. Every grain
Is sentient both in unity and part,
And the minutest atom comprehends
A world of loves and hatreds;[15]

Shelley's belief, or indeed experience, shared with Empedocles and Hölderlin, of a spirit or soul in everything, is poignantly expressed in his poem *The Woodman and the Nightingale*, in which the birds and trees and sea and universe and 'every sphere' are 'awed into delight' by the nightingale's melody – everything, that is, but the rough woodman:

And so this man returned with axe and saw
At evening close from killing the tall treen,
The soul of whom by Nature's gentle law

Was each a wood-nymph, and kept ever green
The pavement and the roof of the wild copse,
Chequering the sunlight of the blue serene

With jaggèd leaves –

Shelley's vision and hope of a new reverence for and union with
Nature, found in so much of his work, echoes the teachings of
Empedocles. Later in *Queen Mab* he writes:

How sweet a scene will earth become!
Of purest spirits a pure dwelling-place,
Symphonious with the planetary spheres;
When man, with changeless Nature coalescing,
Will undertake regeneration's work ...[16]

Compare Empedokles' *'Heiligtum'* speech, given to the people of
Agrigentum before finally leaving them for the slopes of Mount
Etna. I quote a few lines:

and lift, as ones newborn,
Your eyes to divine Nature!

...

Then from the bliss of beautiful dawn
The earth's green grows anew
And Mountain and Sea and Clouds and Stars,
The noble Powers, like Brother-heroes,
Come before your eyes.[17]

Hölderlin obviously felt great empathy with the historical and mythical Empedocles and wrote three versions of his tragedy *Der Tod des Empedokles* which deals with Empedocles' last day on earth. All versions were unfinished, and opinion is divided on the reason for this. I would say that the ultimate reunion with Nature which Empedocles was determined upon was too powerful to represent in a play and also that Hölderlin saw too close a parallel with his own fate of being reviled by the country he loved and had hoped to influence for the betterment of mankind. In his *Grund zum Empedokles* (Argument for Empedokles) Hölderlin describes the character of his hero which could be a portrait of Shelley and of Hölderlin himself:

Nature ... appeared with all her melodies in the spirit and the mouth of this man and so intimately and warm and personal as if his heart were hers, and the Spirit of the Elements lived in human form amongst the mortals.

Empedocles, Hölderlin and Shelley see, through Love,[18] Mother Nature in all her immense and timeless beauty, and all hope for a reconciliation of all beings. In the penultimate scene of Hölderlin's play, from which the above excerpt is taken, Empedocles describes the joining of hands of all peoples which will result from Man's having the courage to be wise, break out of the shackles of 'old Custom' and 'bloody Faith',[19] and thereby gain the gift of seeing, and therefore revering Nature in all her powerful and divine Beauty.

The concept of love in understanding brings me back to Hellingrath and the reception of Hölderlin's work. I would like to quote the editor who completed the collected edition of Hölderlin's work – tragically unfinished by the original editor, Norbert von Hellingrath, who, while working on it, was killed at the age of twenty-eight in the First World War. I translate:

> Unbelievable as it may sound to later generations, the majority of the … poems and fragments of Hölderlin's late work came to light then – a century after their composition – in the middle of the tumult of war …
>
> … Until then they had lain – a preserved treasure – in the dust of public libraries, with no one aware of them, only occasionally found by intrusive, inquisitive people and, with a shaking of heads, ogled and fingered as curiosities and abortive attempts.
>
> To Hellingrath it was granted to extract them from the confused manuscripts … into clarity and order.
>
> In the field of modern *Wissenschaft* Hellingrath's is unique evidence that love in understanding can be more objective, more stringent even, in any case more fruitful and more revealing, than the confidence of prudently distanced, dry or clever scholarship.[20]

In one of the two lectures printed in the above mentioned book, Hellingrath writes of Hölderlin's complete trust, familiarity and oneness with his Gods and of the resulting failure of people to understand his visionary poetry reflecting this:

Hölderlin never flatly told of this heaven, wrote down a divine comedy, but the world of the Gods is always around him, where a word indicates, there it is permanent and ordered around us, as though it bore the belief of a people; for these words speak with brotherly trust of the wonderful world as of something pre-supposed, obvious, known from time immemorial: where this child-like, heart-felt, unbroken belief speaks of it, the Gods are really there ...

He who thus lives amongst Gods, his speech will no longer be understood by people; for the first time in Germany poetic language ventured forth, undissembled, nurtured in native air ... but the Germans did not print it, did not read the great hymns, merely called them 'signs of madness' ...[21]

Hölderlin's work, then, is an elemental song – a celebration of his union with and love of Nature, of the Good and the True and the Beautiful. And if he offers an apology to the reader for unconventional writing, as in *Hyperion* and in the preface to *Friedensfeier* (Celebration of Peace), it is because he is so misunderstood. But, he says, 'I cannot write otherwise. One day almost every form of song will be heard and Nature from whence it came will take it back again to herself.'

BIOGRAPHY

The secure unity and wholeness of Hölderlin's early years amongst his Gods of Nature gradually at first, and then all too quickly, becomes more and more fragmented and shot through with deeply disturbing events which eventually and inevitably lead to his *Umnachtung* (benightment).

Johann Christoph Friedrich Hölderlin was born in 1770, the same year as Beethoven and Wordsworth and his close friend Hegel, in Lauffen am Neckar in the house attached to the monastery where his father was overseer. The family moved when he was four years old to Nürtingen at the foot of the Swabian alps, again on the Neckar, where his mother lived until her death – this was for Hölderlin his home. His father died when he was two and his mother remarried a Herr Gock who became a *Bürgermeister*. But as, after another five years, she was again a widow, Hölderlin, as he grew up, felt, as well as a great bond of love with his mother, a great responsibility as gradually the rift of understanding between them became ever wider; his mother's was essentially a simple, *bürgerlich* outlook and her son was becoming strange to her. Her fervent wish was for Hölderlin to marry and live a quiet life as a priest, preaching the word of God as indeed his fellow ordinand, Ludwig Neuffer, did, demanding, like a Jane Austen cleric, a good cellar and a groaning table! At eighteen, Hölderlin was at the Tübinger Stift where he continued his youthful friendship with the five years younger Schelling and met a new friend, Hegel. The three, together with Magenau and Neuffer, formed a private club in which they discussed set topics and read each other their poetry.

198

All the ordinands were under the powerful influence of Schiller. For Hölderlin, who, in his early poetry, imitated his work, Schiller was a hero and mentor but was soon to have an ambivalently damaging effect on his life.

The messianic pietism of the Swabian mystic Alfred Bengel (a copy of his mystical comment on the New Testament was among the books found in Hölderlin's library),[22] Homer, Sophocles and, above all, Plato formed the spiritual basis of Hölderlin's life in the Stift. Later, at the beginnings of his breakdown, it was being read to from Homer by a young classics scholar that calmed him down. (The Bible however, had 'a very bad effect' on him.) But it was because of his own innate knowledge of Nature that he could follow Plato in the *Timaeus* 'into the depths of the deeps, to the most distant ends of the world of the Spirit, where the Soul of the World sends out its life into the thousand pulses of Nature', and Socrates in the *Symposium* who 'with his divine wisdom' taught him what love was. As an ordinand he was already writing the first draft of *Hyperion* where Melite is the priestess of love – the future Diotima who would appear three years later in 1796 as Susette Gontard. And already he was challenging the Christian dogma of one God. After writing in *Hyperion* in the Third Letter:

Oh you to whom I called, as though you were beyond the stars, whom I called Creator of Heaven and Earth, friendly idol of my childhood, you will not be angry that I forgot you! Why is the world not needy enough to seek another as well?

he adds the apologetic footnote:

> It is probably not necessary to note, that such remarks as
> mere phenomena of the human psyche should by rights
> scandalize no one.

*

His friends at the seminary described Hölderlin as melancholic, moody, gentle; but his bearing, according to one of his first biographers, Schwab, was 'as though Apollo strode through the Great Hall'.[24] Although, at the wish of his mother, Hölderlin stayed at the Tübinger Stift for five years, he rebelled against the spiritual narrowness of orthodox theology, calling the theologians there the *Todtengräber in Tübingen* (gravediggers in Tübingen), whilst Hegel called them *mechanische Köpfe* (mechanical heads). The young Hölderlin was like a volcano tired of its imprisonment in the earth. Not until the freeing influence of Susette Gontard, to whom he confessed he had given up philosophy, does Hölderlin write of his early days in *Da ich ein Knabe war* (When I was a boy):

> When I was a boy
> A God rescued me often
> From the clamour and whips of men
> Then, secure and good, I played
> With the flowers of the grove
> And the breezes of Heaven
> Played with me.

And as you delight
The heart of the plants
When they stretch towards you
Their tender arms

So have you delighted my heart
Father Helios! and like Endymion
I was your belovèd
Holy Luna!

Oh all you faithful
Friendly Gods
If only you knew
How my soul loved you.

True, I had not yet called
You by name, nor you
Named me, as men name each other
As though they knew one another.

But I knew you better
Than I had ever known men,
I understood the stillness of the Aether,
The words of men I never understood.

I was brought up by the melody
Of the rustling woods
And to love I learnt
Amongst the flowers.

In the arms of the Gods I grew up.

*

At the beginning of the French Revolution, Hölderlin is writing,

> Freedom must eventually come, and Virtue will be better able to flourish in the holy warming Light of Freedom, than in the ice-cold Zone of Despotism.
>
> … That is the holy goal of my wishes and my occupation, that in our time I awake the seed that will flourish in the future.[25]

The three friends, Hölderlin, Hegel and Schelling, arrived at the pantheistic formula *Eins und All* (One and All).[26] Their password was *Reich Gottes!* and years later when Hegel and Hölderlin came together they met with their password.

At the storming of the Bastille in 1793 it is said that Hölderlin, Schelling and Hegel erected a Tree of Liberty on the banks of the Rhine and danced round it. They were also under suspicion of having translated the *Marseillaise*. Later at the beginning of his breakdown Hölderlin kept saying *'Ich will kein Jakobiner sein'* … His friend, Sinclair, had been on trial for suspected Jacobin sympathies and then imprisoned in the Solitude, and his friend and first publisher, Stäudlin, had committed suicide in the Rhine because of his despair at the outcome of the Revolution. All this terrible violence and despair was the backdrop to Hölderlin's vision of a New World of Truth and Love and Beauty. And a hundred years later the First World War was to be the tragic background to Hellingrath's discovery and publication of Hölderlin.

In the winter of 1794 Hölderlin, having left the Stift, is a student of philosophy at the University of Jena – earning money as a house tutor to the son of Charlotte von Kalb, a friend of Schiller's. He is fascinated by Fichte's lectures, but eventually repelled, and a frequent guest of his hero, Schiller, who publishes Hölderlin's *Fragment von Hyperion* in his *Thalia*. On his first visit to Schiller there is another person in the room whom he does not recognize as he is completely taken up with Schiller. There is a copy of *Thalia* containing his *Fragment* lying on a table. The stranger silently flicks through it, causing Hölderlin to become *über und über rot,* as he writes – very red. That evening at the *Klub der Professoren* he learns that Goethe had been at Schiller's!

In March, Schiller recommends *Hyperion* to the publisher Cotta, who pays Hölderlin 'child's money' for it.

At the end of May 1795, he flees from Jena, making a sudden appearance at home, driven away as he says by 'the airy spirits with metaphysical wings', the oppressive weight of Schiller and Fichte. After being with Schiller, Hölderlin wrote in a letter, the next day he was unable to think or do anything. It is interesting to note here the answer of the Soothsayer to Antony's question of whose fortunes shall rise higher:

Cæsar's
Therefore, O Antony, stay not by his side:
Thy demon, that's thy spirit which keeps thee, is
Noble, courageous, high, unmatchable,
Where Cæsar's is not; but, near him, thy angel
Becomes a fear, as being o'erpowered; therefore
Make space enough between you.[27]

This is what happened to Hölderlin. Jena and its 'Titans' nearly overpowered his angel and he had to escape.

For Hölderlin, it is the Absolute or the God between I and Thou that is important, and to him the Fichtean Ego – Non-Ego remained on the material plane.[28] And when one thinks of one's closest friends or family it often is not what is said but the 'tones' that sing between you that is the reality, the real relationship, which then stretches into the eternal. In a letter to his half-brother in November 1798, Hölderlin writes:

> And from time to time we must bring the offering to the Divinity that is between you and me.

And later to Böhlendorff he writes:

> I need your pure tones. The psyche amongst friends, the formation of thought through conversation and letters is necessary to artists.[29]

*

When Hölderlin entered the Gontard household in Frankfurt as tutor to their son, Henry, at the beginning of January 1796, he was entering the most important and tragic era of his life. He was to meet the embodiment of all that he believed in, the Melite of the earlier draft of *Hyperion,* the Diotima of Plato's *Symposium,* Gontard's wife, Susette. This was no ordinary love. It was a meeting of two souls who were inextricably bound. When they were forced to part, they lost themselves unto death. As Ronald Peacock points out when discussing Hölderlin's most movingly beautiful elegy, *Menons Klagen um Diotima*:

> *Lycidas, Adonais* and *Thyrsis,* to recall famous elegies of English literature, are all, like *Euphrosyne*, laments for the death of a friend, the early death and the blighting of hopes; and their authors, it is true, incorporate in them much of their general philosophy. *Menons Klagen* are a lament for the loss of life itself
>
> … Milton and Shelley, Arnold and Goethe, bewail personal loss, but not the loss of themselves …

> Aber das Haus ist öde mir nun, und sie haben mein Auge
> Mir genommen, auch mich hab' ich verloren mit ihr.
> Darum irr' ich umher, und wohl, wie die Schatten, so muß ich
> Leben, und sinnlos dünkt lange das Übrige mir.[30]

The lines preceding this quotation (translated below) again contain Hölderlin's belief in, and experience of, the God between or amongst us:

> But we, peacefully joined, like the loving swans,
> When they rest on the lake, or, rocked by waves
> Look down into the water, where silver clouds mirror themselves,
> And ethereal blue undulates under the travellers in ships,
> So on earth we wandered. And even if the North threatened
> He, the enemy of lovers, tendering laments, and fell

From the branches the leaves, and flew in the wind the rain
  Quietly we smiled, were aware of our God
In our trusting conversation; in one soul-song
  Completely at peace with ourselves, childish and joyfully alone.
But the house is laid waste for me now, and they have taken my eye
  From me, also myself I have lost with her.
Thus I wander about, and perhaps like the Shades, so must I
  Live, and senseless, long has seemed the rest to me.

This was written in 1800, two years after their parting.

In September 1798 he leaves the Gontard household after aggressive words with Herr Gontard. Little Henry is heartbroken. Susette and Hölderlin continue to have secret meetings. 'Without you my life slowly fades away and slowly dies,' writes Susette prophetically.

At the time of his dismissal Hölderlin has already begun working on *Empedokles* and is planning a journal, *Iduna*, which could support him rather than the humiliating servant capacity jobs of house tutor. He thinks of going to Jena to try again for a university post in Greek Literature, but Schiller has already advised him against this. At the end of October the second volume of *Hyperion* is published. There is a fleeting meeting with Susette when he gives her the volume inscribed *Wem sonst als Dir*, accompanied with the complaint,

It is terrible to think that we both with our best strength must perhaps perish because we lack each other.

206

In 1800 Hölderlin is once again declining his Mother's advice to take a church living, still hoping that his journal will materialize and bring an income.

In February there is a last meeting of Hölderlin and his Diotima.

In February 1801 the Peace of Lunéville inspires *Friedensfeier*, in which Hölderlin invites all the Gods and prophets to a celebration in the Natural Church of Nature where Time has lost its power. The poem was not discovered or published until 1954. It incorporates his hopes of the bringing together of Christ with the older Gods and Divine Nature at the End of Time – but the expected 'Prince of the Feast' for whom the Divine Celebration has been prepared is unnamed and could be Christ or the prophet of the New Religion spoken of in *Hyperion* that will come:

> … when … the last, most beautiful Daughter of Time, the new Church, comes forth out of these stained outmoded forms, when the awakened feeling for the Divine brings back to man his divinity and to his breast beautiful youth …

In 1802 *Menons Klagen um Diotima* is published – badly!

In May Hölderlin writes his letter to Schiller asking him to help him get a post in Jena as a lecturer in Greek Literature. Schiller does not reply.

In the Summer Cotta is ready to publish his poems (at a price) but first wants a 'favourite poem' as advertisement to be published in his *Damenkalender*. Nothing comes of it.

Hölderlin's health and state of mind are beginning to show signs of breaking. His friend Sinclair tries to do what he can for him and in the Autumn a house tutor post in Bordeaux is arranged at the home of the Hamburg Konsul, Meyer.

On the 4th December Hölderlin writes to Böhlendorff:

> I am now full of parting, perhaps for ever. For what have I more dear in the world? But they do not want me. German, however, I will and must remain, even if the heart and living necessity drove me to Otaheite.

About the 10th December he leaves Nürtingen – on foot – for Bordeaux.

On the 15th December he is held as a foreigner in Strasbourg until the 30th and told not to go through Paris but to register with the police.

At the beginning of January 1803 he makes a difficult journey to Lyon – treacherous cold weather and flooding. On the 28th January he arrives.

In the middle of May he departs. His biographers write that it is not known why. But to me the cause seems clear.

In the middle of June he arrives in Stuttgart – exhausted, wild-eyed, clad like a beggar and, apparently, out of his mind. In the middle of June (the 22nd) Susette dies nursing her children with German measles but also, it is written, of consumption and loneliness. Sinclair writes to Hölderlin in Bordeaux of her death, thinking him still to be there. Hölderlin receives the letter in Stuttgart at the beginning of July. His elegy *Achill* (Achilles) written in 1798 immediately after the parting from Susette Gontard and before the Bordeaux tutorship, throws light on his state of mind there:

Glorious Son of the Gods! when you had lost the belovèd
    You went to the shore of the sea, wept out into the flood,
Lamenting, desired descent into the holy depth,
    In the stillness, your heart, where, from the noise of the ships
Far, deep under the waves, in a peaceful grotto the blue
    Thetis lived, who protected you, the Sea-goddess.
Mother she was to the youth, the powerful Goddess,
    Had once suckled the child, lovingly on the rocky
Shores of his island, with the forceful song of the waves
    And in the strengthening bath had made him a Hero.
And the mother perceived the lament of the youth,
    Rose up from the bed of the sea mourning, like clouds,
Quietened with tender embrace the pains of the loved-one,
    And he heard, how she caressingly promised to help.

Son of the Gods! O were I like you so could I trustingly
    To one of the Gods complain of my secret grief.
I must not see it, must bear the disgrace as though I had
    Never belonged to her, who yet thinks of me with tears.
Good Gods! yet you hear each plea of man,
    Oh, and deeply and purely I loved you Holy Light,
All my life, you Earth and your Springs and Woods,
    Father Aether, and felt you too yearningly and purely
This heart – oh soften for me, you Good Ones, my suffering,
    So my soul does not become for me silent too soon,
So that I may live and you, you high Divine powers
    Even on the fleeting day, I may thank with pious song
Thank for previous blessings, for joy of past youth,
    And then take up to you, kindly, the lonely one.

That was in 1798. In 1805 Charlotte von Kalb is writing to Jean Paul of Hölderlin:

> This man is now raving mad; however his *Geist* has reached a level that only a seer, one indwelt by God, can reach.

CONCLUSION

Hölderlin's fate is the fate of a seer. The tragic figure of Cassandra springs to mind, daughter of Hecuba, seer and prophet but doomed by the slighted Apollo never to be believed but instead to be looked on as insane. Hölderlin, the prophet of the Divine, who in *Hyperion* and *Der Tod des Empedokles* gives so many wise indications of what will happen if we lose our faith in Nature is, apart from a few friends and admirers, ignored, thought of as mad. Schiller had given him up. Goethe had dismissed him. His mother did not understand him. Even amongst his Stift friends, he was, in essence, *'ohne Genossen'*.

> *Indessen dünket mir öfters*
> *Besser zu schlafen, wie so ohne Genossen zu seyn,*
> *So zu harren, und was zu thun indeß und zu sagen,*
> *Weiß ich nicht, und wozu Dichter in dürftiger Zeit.*

> Meanwhile it seems to me often
> Better to sleep, than be so companionless,
> Thus to expectantly wait, and what to do meanwhile and to say,
> I know not, and why poet in barren times?[31]

A parallel could be seen here with Shelley's *Stanzas Written in Dejection near Naples*, but with Hölderlin the significance of 'sleep' is fundamental to his reason for existence. To 'sleep' would mean giving up his vocation of a poet, whom he sees as entrusted with the gift of *Heilig Gedächtnis* (holy memory), and therefore, the task of 'staying awake by night'.

In his last great poems Hölderlin is struggling with the idea that in the time of darkness that has enveloped us since the last of the Gods, Christ, left us, we have had to suffice with the symbols of their presence, *Brod* and *Wein*. And that it is the poet's task, as I said at the beginning of this paper, to remain watching or awake by night – *wachend zu bleiben bei Nacht*, as Hölderlin writes in the second stanza of *Brod und Wein*. He is using the word *wachen*, 'to watch/keep awake', in full awareness of St Matthew's Gospel, in the Greek and as translated by Luther. His language now resembles the last quartets of Schubert in its bare and piercing honesty.

Hölderlin's *Umnachtung* or benightment is not separate but part of his life as a seer. He tried to reconcile his vision with the world around him and could not. He saw, above Time, like all the great mystics, the coming together of all things, a reconciliation of the apparently irreconcilable – Christ with the Ancient Gods, Greece with Germany, Man with Nature and, most importantly, Nature as Divine; and wrote, as in *Friedensfeier*, of the advent of a New Religion or state of Timelessness when the veil of the World is lifted, death departs and the divine world of *Gesang* is imminent. This divine vision he translated into song, thereby rendering the revelation unharmful to man. But he, the conductor of the lightning, was finally struck dumb and remained silent for the last thirty-six years of his life. Like Antigone (one of his last works was a translation of Sophocles' play), he obeyed a law beyond that of mortals, a law not understood by the Creons of this world. For him *dichten*, to write poetry, was synonymous with *danken*, to thank.

His story reads like a myth. Educated from an early age in monastery schools in fairy-tale seclusion in the depths of Swabia by austere pietistic clergy, and then five years' imprisonment in the Tübinger Stift, another ancient unheated building where snow and rain would sometimes settle in the spartan rooms, immersed in the Bible and the Classics – his whole training preparing him, as his mother wished, to be a minister of the Word of God – and then rebellion. His reputed dancing round a *Freiheitsbaum* on the banks of the Rhine with Hegel and Schelling could be seen not only as a celebration of the French Revolution and Freedom but a celebration of his own Revolution and bid for Freedom. Freedom to talk about the Gods that he knew, and knew intimately by instinct and enthusiasm and vision and not by rote. But then, *Wozu dichten in dürftiger Zeit?*

Like all his heroes, Antigone, Oedipus, Empedocles, Achilles, he was not understood, was lonely and isolated in the fragmented and material world of men. In Jena, Fichte, it seemed, was lecturing on man's superiority over Nature; Schiller, his hero, lost interest in him, he and Goethe calling him *ein Poetchen* – the diminutive form of Poet; and then the great Goethe's advice – to restrict himself to *kleine Gedichte*!

And if this were not enough, to have to earn his living as a beggar in his own house, the Germany he was trying to revivify – to be a paid servant in the houses of the wealthy, where as he wrote in a letter to his half-brother, they mainly disported themselves like *Bauern* with *neuer Wein*, peasants with new wine. And still to continue writing with praise and wonder some of the greatest poetry ever written. Then in one of these despised households to meet his Diotima, the Melite of the *Fragment von Hyperion* which Schiller had published in his *Thalia* and which Goethe silently and slightingly flicked through while Hölderlin stood speechlessly looking on. To meet his other self, like Plato's two halves of a Whole, to come together like two rivers rushing into one sea and then, two years later, to be forced to part. It is like a fairy tale.

The correspondence between Hölderlin and Susette that has come down to us shows the oneness of vision there was between them. Both were musical, Hölderlin a flautist and Susette a pianist. Their relationship was like a Divine Song – there are so many references in Hölderlin's work to *Töne, Gesang* and *Melodie* regarding his relationship with Susette and with Nature.

Rarely in his days in the *Turm* on the banks of the Neckar in Tübingen with the caring and understanding Master Carpenter Zimmer, who had read and liked *Hyperion*, did he talk of the past. He withdrew completely, addressing those inquisitive, horrible visitors in an old-fashioned polite style and calling himself outlandish names like 'Scardanelli'. His few letters to his mother are in a stilted, childish German. It seemed that the past was past. But Susette was always with him, part of him. Once, apparently, when the name of his 'Diotima' was mentioned to him by a visitor, the now seventy-one-year-old Hölderlin said in simple Swabian dialect, '*Närret isch se worde.*' She became mad.

To me Hölderlin was, like his writing, an instrument. Schelling said that he was *sehr zart gestimmt* (very delicately strung). He sang with his whole being, and when the burden of his song became too much to bear, the Gods took pity on him, broke the lyre and led him into the peaceful shadows of night.

NOTES

1 'There will be only One Beauty; and Mankind and Nature will unite in One all-embracing Divinity' (*Hyperion*, Zweiter Band, Erstes Buch).

2 'All forms are similar, and not one resembles the other' (*Elegien,*Zweites Buch: *Goethes Werke: Hamburger Ausgabe*, ed. Erich Trunz (8th printing: Hamburg, 1966), l.99).

3 Ronald Peacock, *Hölderlin* (London, 1938), p. 1.

4 I have adopted the practice of M.B.Benn and my former tutor, Robin Harrison, of using 'Empedocles' to refer to the historical and mythical Empedocles and 'Empedokles' to refer to the hero of Hölderlin's play. See Harrison's *Hölderlin and Greek Literature* (Oxford, 1975).

5 In an interview given last year from Highgrove on Easter Day, marking the sixtieth anniversary of *Gardener's Question Time*, Prince Charles expressed similar sentiments: we 'zone everything', he said, and there is 'no integration'.

6 *Hyperion*, Zweiter Band, Zweites Buch.

7 Theodor Storm, *Immensee und andere Novellen* (Frankfurt am Main, 1983), p. 32.

8 See Thrasybulos Georgiades, *Musik und Rhythmus bei den Griechen – Zum Ursprung der abendländischen Musik* (Hamburg, 1958).

9 I wrote this before hearing Dr Rowan Williams talking about Herbert and Vaughan and saying that it is the music that is

left with one after reading, say, *The World.*

10 'Plato, Shamanism and Ancient Egypt', *Temenos Academy Review 9* (2006) p. 86

11 Empedocles, Fragment 6/129, translated Brad Inwood, *The Poem of Empedocles* (Toronto, 2001), p. 205

12 Percy Bysshe Shelley, *Marenghi* xxiii.

13 Fragment 123/30: Inwood, op.cit, p. 259

14 Cited ibid., p. 138.

15 Queen Mab IV.

16 Queen Mab VI.

17 *Der Tod des Empedokles* II iv

18 Cf. Shelley, *A Defence of Poetry:* 'The great secret of mortals is love; or a going out of our own nature, and an identification of ourselves with the beautiful which exists in thought, action, or person, not our own.' See also his translation of Plato's *Symposium* concerning the Beauty of the God of Love.

19 Idem, *Feelings of a Republican on the Fall of Bonaparte:* 'I know/Too late, since thou and France are in the dust,/That Virtue owns a more eternal foe/Than Force or Fraud: old Custom, legal Crime,/And bloody Faith the foulest birth of Time.'

20 Ludwig von Pigenot, in the introduction to Norbert von Hellingrath, *Hölderlin: Zwei Vorträge* (Munich, 1921), pp. 9-11.

21 From lecture notes not prepared for publication but published by Pigenot in memory of Hellingrath: ibid., pp. 61,62.

22 This included Friedrich Heinrich Jacobi's *Über die Lehre des Spinoza,* through which, it is interesting to note, Hölderlin became acquainted with the theories of Giordano Bruno.

23 This is a direct reference to the effect of Fichte's teaching on Hölderlin. Following his notes on this exclamatory sentence, Friedrich Beissner cites, from the metrical draft of *Hyperion,* the phrase Tyrannisch *gegen die Natur* ('tyrannical towards Nature') with the comment, 'This is Fichte's teaching, in which the ego posits itself and those Things outside itself, particularly Nature, are defined as non-ego.' At first Hölderlin writes enthusiastically about Fichte's lectures but with the realization of the philosopher's diametrically opposed view of Nature comes Hölderlin's flight from Jena and the *Luftgeister mit metaphysischen Flügeln.*

24 Cited by Ulrich Häussermann, *Hölderlin* (Hamburg, 1961), p. 50: '*Sein Auftreten war – nach der Überlieferung durch Schwab – "als schritte Apollo durch den Saal"*'.

25 From a letter to his half-brother Karl Gock, September 1793.

26 έν και παν, which appears in the fourth volume of Jacobi, *Briefe,* cited in n. 22 above.

27 *Antony and Cleopatra* II iii.

28 'The encounter with the Partner gives man the experience of his reality – this is valid for Fichte as for Hölderlin. But the starting points are different. Fichte's sole interest is so directed that man comes about (*sich macht)* through the fulfilment of his field of energy (his particular 'sphere'). He posits himself (*setzt sich*) through the establishment of the opposite

(*Gegensatz*; Natural Law). Hölderlin's sole interest in the encounter with the fateful *Du* is to participate in the Third Part, the Absolute, that is between me and thee (*zwischen mir und Dir*). Hölderlin's thinking stops abruptly here and passes directly into reverence, whilst Fichte's is methodically directed towards action' (Häussermann, *Hölderlin*; see also n. 24 above). For the God or Absolute, between us, compare the above quotations and the passage from *Menons Klagen um Diotima* translated above.

29   It is interesting to note Kleist's essay of 1805 *Über die allmähliche Verfertigung der Gedanken beim Reden* (On the Gradual Completion of Thought through Discourse).

30   Peacock, *Hölderlin,* Chapter VII 'Diotima'.

31   *Brot und Wein*, stanza vii.

Hölderlin's Retreat into Darkness

No, not for long can one endure the piercing shaft
The sudden searing through the body of lightning recognition
The leap to meet the all-consuming flame.

Not long can one remain, like Socrates, a smiling citizen of the
world
Polite and conscientious, paying taxes, teaching
Whilst suddenly, at any time, this
Dreadful agony darts through one, beaming strange,
penetrating light
Upon the glowing vision
As though one stood upon a magic pinnacle
And saw the All spread out in contour,
Saw suddenly Dionysus, Christ and Buddha, Empedocles
Calling for kind peace, cessation of blood-shed, saw all Divines
All Lovers, Hero and Leander and the shrouding Hellespont
Cleopatra clasping death to her wild, mourning breast,
Saw wondrous Nature in Her unity, the soaring tree and busy ant
The yawning crocodile and caring ape, divine winged creatures,
The holy water-dwellers, all haloed in embracing Aether,
Saw again one's childhood vision of the splendour in the grass,
While far below in stinking caves the greedy creeping cruelty of man

Tries desperately to destroy it.
Not long can one stand on the threshold of Eternity
Conducting holy fire.
Something will break.

Frightened jealous fools will offer hemlock, murderous assault, a cross.
Drunkenness or madness will draw down the blind
Leaving the poet distanced,
Smiling at visitors to his quiet abode
Smiling beyond their prying, stupid stares
Smiling towards a terrible, aching void
                                        that is his own
Whilst in the untenanted hall of his great mind
Soft shadows murmur ceaselessly.